THE EMPEROR'S
LAST SOLDIERS

THE EMPEROR'S LAST SOLDIERS

By Itō Masashi

TRANSLATED BY ROGER CLIFTON

COWARD-McCANN, Inc.
NEW YORK

Contents

PART I

Sea, Sky, Islands

PART II

The Jungle

PART III

Sky, Base and Home

Illustrations will be found following page 98

I

SEA, SKY, ISLANDS

1

To the Front

I was summoned to appear before the draft board a few
months before the outbreak of the Pacific war. It was in
1941: the Sino-Japanese incident looked as though it was
going to develop into a protracted conflict; Germany had
invaded Poland in Europe; and nearer at home the Japanese army had initiated a series of new operations on the
Chinese mainland—there were fresh moves in the western
part of Shansi province in October, followed a month later
by vigorous activity in Shantung. I was hardly surprised,
therefore, after I had taken the various tests, to hear the
officer in charge of conscription pronounce firmly: "Pass!
...A.1. ..."

When I got home, the whole village turned out to congratulate me on the result.

I realised that once I enlisted I should eventually be sent
to the front, and I already knew that my draft would not be
called until the January of the following year. So I set myself the task of preparing my mind and accustoming myself
to the idea as best I could during the interval. Then, about
a month before I was due to leave, the Pacific war began.

"The Imperial Army and Navy, before dawn this day,
December 8th, entered into a state of hostility in the
Western Pacific with British and American forces...." It
was seven o'clock in the morning. The communiqué was
read time and again on the radio. Later, at 11.40 the same

morning, the Imperial Edict embracing the official declaration of war was broadcast. I listened, absorbed, my whole being concentrated on the words coming from the brown loudspeaker on the table, To this day, I remember vividly how my mother's and father's eyes remained riveted on my face as I listened.

On 10 January, 1942, to the waving of flags and shouts of "Good luck!", my friend Aihara Fumiya and I, together with other conscripts from our village, left to enlist in the East 63rds at Kofu. Little did any of us realise that, alone among those young men, *I* was to embark upon a "war" which was to last me for almost nineteen years!

When we enlisted, the unit was in high spirits. Morale was good as a result of a string of Japanese victories. Training was conducted, however, with no let-up in discipline—the usual dreary round of strictness, routine, square-bashing, assault courses, and orders, orders, orders. Then, after the inspection parade which terminated this initial period of impersonal, unfriendly training, I was posted with a crowd of fellow draftees to a unit in Jimmu-tun, in the Amur River Province in Manchuria. By a stroke of good fortune which did much to alleviate the strangeness of those early days, my friend Aihara was still with me.

In July I was promoted to the rank of Private First Class. Then, in April of 1943, we were ordered to move to Peian. Being in the higher grade meant that the daily chores and duties of a second-line unit impinged less on one's freedom and there was much less hardship than before. The days—even the weeks and months—slipped by.

In the front line, nevertheless, there was fierce fighting day after day. Japanese forces everywhere were being driven on to the defensive. The American troops who had taken Guadalcanal, the men who boasted that they always fought every encounter to the bitter end, seemed almost to be combing the entire South Seas for us Japanese "lice". They attacked the Bismarcks from the Solomons and appeared to be trying to work themselves into a position from which they could command a strike to the north. For us, however, there was no way of finding out how the progress of the war in general was going: we simply had to wait until it was our turn for the front-line. With our eyes fixed on the ultimate victory we were certain would be ours, we spent from sunrise to sunset every day, training and training.

Early in March, 1944, we received a sudden and unexpected order to move. We had no means of finding out where—but we judged from the kit issued to us that it must be in the south. By this time I was a Lance-Corporal, a gunner in a light machine-gun crew. Our Division, newly constituted, had been formed from the two mixed Brigades, "Lightning" and "Prosperity", under the command of Lieut. General Takashina. Among the other commanders whose names still come to mind were Lieut. General Obata, in charge of Divisional H.Q., Tamura, who was second-in-command, Staff, and one Tsukamoto, another Staff Officer. I was attached to a unit comprising 102nd Uno and 2556 Prosperity: at Battalion strength there was the Takeuchi, at Company strength the Imai, and there was the Asada Section. Best of all, good old Aihara was posted to the very same unit! Indeed, most of the men in the new unit were from places in our regimental recruiting areas back home— Toyohashi, Kofu, Sakura and Akasaka, one of the wards of Tokyo. It was the sort of composite, Fred Karno mob you'd expect and often saw formed under emergency conditions at the height of the war.

2

We Land on Guam

We stayed for a day in Yokohama Bay, loading vast quantities of stores and ammunition. Then our Corps left the wharf in a convoy of thirteen ships. It was mid-March, and—judging from the evasive action we took—an open season for enemy submarines! We struck south along the Marianas, through the central Pacific, and eventually reached a point off Guam, which lies at the extreme southern tip of the Marianas chain, on March 21st.

Looking back now on the war situation as it was then, and in particular on the operations in the Central Pacific Zone, I can see we never had much of a chance on Guam— which had originally been under American administration anyway. United States forces had already gained complete control of the Marshall Islands and were preparing an assault on the Philippines, while in the eastern part of the Zone, Allied forces were really stepping up operations on the New Guinea front. The enemy's superiority in the air was marked. The burden of defensive preparations against all this therefore lay heavily on the two mixed Brigades forming our Division.

The island of Guam, the largest in the Marianas group, is about 350 square miles in area, just a little smaller than our island of Awaji in Japan. It is long and narrow, stretching almost thirty miles from north to south. At its thinnest point, it is no more than four miles across. Our Army Corps disembarked without incident and with never a shot fired in anger. We came ashore at a place to which we gave the name Harbour Town, lying between Sheep Island and the village of Sumai.

For a month and a half, our unit was stationed in the area of the River Inada, near the southernmost tip of the island. We spent every available hour from dawn to dusk preparing our positions, and in battle practice. Then, early in May, out of the blue, the unit was dispersed over the whole island and set on a battle footing.

The Battalion to which Aihara and I were attached was stationed in the centre of Guam, looking out over the east coast, with Battalion H.Q. sited on the headwaters of the River Hakoya. My Company was located on a plateau commanding the vicinity of the Talofofo estuary—the river taking a course south from the Battalion H.Q. area. Here we took up battle positions, with the waters of the Talofofo flowing fast and full before our eyes.

This was the largest river on the island, with a width, where we were, of something over twenty yards. We spent what little free time we had in swimming and catching a type of fish rather like an eel which swam upriver. It was a disagreeable looking creature; sometimes we caught them as much as four or five feet long and measuring five inches or more in diameter. If one of them managed to get itself coiled around a hand or foot, it would cling and squeeze with a force that was unnerving and frightening—but we would climb out of the water with the eels still coiled around us, and of course their fate was to end up on our table! A dish of eels broiled in oil was a tasty addition to wartime rations.... When we had the time, we would also amuse ourselves by following the river right down to the beach and go fishing for octopus. Now and again on these expeditions we would catch sight of the canoes of the Chamorro, the aboriginals of Guam.

But for the ever-present reminder of the butchery of war, I suppose it could have been called a peaceful, pleasant existence. It was not to last long, however.

Very soon after the beginning of May, we heard our first air raid warning. Soon we were able to recognise the silhouettes of enemy aircraft. During the raids, the only thing we could do was to shelter in one of the natural caves or hollows set among the rocky crags. In the rugged hinterland of Guam there were innumerable natural depressions of this nature, and those in the Talofofo basin, which were of all sizes and shapes, dotted everywhere along the valley, formed quite the best air raid shelters we could find.

The sirens disturbed us every day at the same hour. But the enemy planes seemed to be ignoring Guam itself: all they did was to fly across the sky from south to north and disappear into the blue. Then, eventually, we would see them coming back on the return trip.

"That's a reconnaissance plane: he won't be dropping any bombs on us," we would reassure one another anxiously, trying to believe it was true as we strained our eyes on the distant silhouette winging its way back to some unknown base far to the south.

"Yes," someone else would always say, "but it's a warning that we'll soon be having bombers flying this way...."

Towards the end of May, our Battalion was moved to a place called Orita, where the H.Q. of "Prosperity" was situated, as a reserve unit. We suspected this had something to do with the belief that, when the Americans did invade, they would land somewhere on the central part of the west coast. Then, on June 11th, we received our baptism of bombing. The explosions shook the whole island and warned us that the time of actual fighting could not be far off. This particular raid, however, did hardly any damage.

From that day on, though, the raids were repeated— every day and every night. The Americans' main concentration, however, seemed to be on the island of Saipan, with Guam, as it were, being leapfrogged. This was particularly obvious on the 15th, when from the very early morning planes began passing overhead on their way north, waves upon waves of them, in such numbers that we lost count. From before dawn on that day we could hear the sound of distant gun-fire, like thunder beyond the horizon, making the earth tremble and quake. Then, as the sun rose in the sky, the intensity of the bombardment grew and grew until finally it had turned into a continuous, nerve-racking vibration that seemed to jar the very bones in our bodies. There was no doubt about it, we thought as we licked our dry lips and eyed each other fearfully: the Americans had by-passed Guam and launched an all-out assault on Saipan.

"My God! Just listen to that ... now I know what a naval bombardment really means," someone whispered as we strained our ears towards the sound of incessant gun-fire which floated, rolling and echoing, across the two-hundred mile stretch of waves separating us from Saipan. "And you

16

can bet anything you like that we'll be next on the list...."

Secretly, we were all thinking the same thing. Our officers became agitated and tense. And the fear became reflected in our Orders for the Day, which grew increasingly severe; preparations redoubled to the point of frenzy; and for us, waiting, the strain grew unbearable.

But that was all we could do: sit tight and wait for them to come at us. There was no other choice.

3

I Lose My Comrade in Arms

By July, overflights of enemy planes were becoming more and more intense. With hardly a gap between the waves of bombers, air raid followed air raid, hour after hour, day after day, time without number every twenty-four hours. The impatience and irritation which grow, fungus-like, on a unit forced on the defensive spread like a disease over our entire force; the orders grew each day more harsh and violent. The enemy planes, in that they held an undisputed mastery of the air, gambolled about above us at will, for all the world as though they were fooling about over a private airfield in peacetime. And with every day the frequency of the attacks increased.

On July 14th, almost immediately after the second wave had passed overhead, a formation of enemy aircraft began yet another attack. We ground troops had not waited for the order to disperse: long before it came we had scattered hell-for-leather in the direction of our cave shelters, thoroughly demoralised!

But this was a raid I shall never forget. For during it my friend Aihara was seriously wounded. Faithful Aihara, the bosom friend with whom I had shared everything that was good and everything that was bad in army life right from

17

the very day we had joined up together; Aihara, the kind of friend who could never be replaced, fell a victim to a bomb splinter—a wicked, jagged piece of metal which entered the rear part of his body and cleaved a path right through him practically to his spine. It was a miracle he wasn't killed outright.

He was given first-aid treatment on the spot by field ambulance men, and then taken back at once to the field hospital, which was sited in the middle of a jungle depression getting on for two miles from our H.Q. Every day, I watched for the chance to scrounge enough time to visit him. As I sat at his bedside on the third and fourth days, I could almost see him wasting away and sinking before my eyes. On the evening of the sixth day, he grabbed hold of my arm; with an ashen face turned weakly to mine, he croaked: "I'm never going to pull round from this one, you know."

"Don't be an idiot!" I said as convincingly as I could. "Of course you'll pull through. They've got the splinter out, you know; and it missed all the vital parts. You'll be all right; you see."

Aihara shook his head weakly.

"Now come on," I said again with forced cheerfulness. "You're going to live through the lot, my boy! It's not written on your cards to die in a hole like—"

"Itō, Itō"—Aihara cut me short, his voice frail and feeble —"Promise me one thing. If the worst should happen, and if you ever manage to get back to Japan alive, promise me you'll go and tell my parents and my sister for me? Promise?"

"Oh, come off it! Let's have no more of this nonsense. I tell you you're going to be all right. You're not going to die. Understand?"

"If you say so. But I have a feeling you're wrong—one way or another, this island will be the death of me." His eyes glazed with a far-away stare. "Look—don't get me wrong: I don't want to saddle you with my dying wish or any of that rot. But if I should ... and if you ... did ever get back ... you *would* go and see my family and tell them how I ... died in action, wouldn't you?"

I cleared my throat. He was gazing at me with pathetic intensity. "Don't *worry* about it," I said roughly. "We'll come through many more scrapes together yet!—But *if* such a thing happened, why of course I would. I promise. Didn't each of us promise the other that if such a thing happened ..." I looked firmly into his unflinching stare, but, try as I would, I couldn't get another word out. And inside I was weeping.

"All right," he sighed, his voice no more than a whisper. "That's all right, then...."

When next I managed to visit the field hospital the following afternoon, Aihara had gone. "Last night," the orderly said, glancing around the darkened room. "And five others with him."

The place was a tangle of confusion. It looked more like one of our cave shelters than a hospital ward.

4

The Enemy Assault

On the 21st of July the sirens screamed even before it was light. The steady succession of air attacks that followed showed a persistence that was quite different from any of the raids we had had before. More and more, the feeling that This was It showed on all our faces. And, as if in confirmation of our fears, a message came through that large-scale enemy units had been sighted already at a point some distance from the western coast of Guam.

Our unit was given the order to move. We began threading our way through the dense jungle covering the hills towards the south. Our objective was the high ground forming the centre of the island's southern half—a wild area including the 1000-foot Mount Tenjó, the highest peak on the island, and Mount Honda, which rose to about 650 feet. We used the name Mount Mangan to describe the whole hilly complex.

Before we got there, however, the naval bombardment started: it overlapped the last assault waves from the air and was the nearest approach to Hell that I shall ever experience. The din robbed us totally of all sense of hearing. It wasn't the same as a boom or a roar that splits the ears: it was more like being imprisoned inside a huge metal drum that was incessantly and insufferably being beaten with a thousand iron hammers. Fortunately for us, we were moving away from the main target area—so although the noise was unbearable, not all that many shells burst close to us.

At 11.30, the Americans landed troops at two separate points—Agana Bay and Agato Bay. From our commanding heights, we watched as flotilla after flotilla, so many that we lost count, of amphibious landing craft forged in towards the shore. Yet there was not a sound from the Japanese defences! Every single cannon, field gun and machine gun on the island maintained a silence as of the dead! All the boom and rumble came from the enemy—from their naval batteries out at sea, from the explosions of the shells around us, from the crunch of bombs dropped by their planes. We were still awaiting the order to attack....

There was a reason for this. Our Staff wished to guard against a repeat performance of what had happened at Saipan. The Japanese had been unable to mount a counter-attack there—because, before the troops even landed, we had committed every single man, every weapon, against the task force bombarding us from sea and air, and against the amphibious assault landing craft surging like ants towards the beaches. Only it happened that these craft were decoys —and when the enemy mounted his real landing assault elsewhere, the defending Japanese had almost exhausted

20

their ammunition and the Americans were able to take the island without encountering any serious opposition.

We could not afford the luxury of a second blunder of this magnitude; our Staff were not going to permit themselves to be fooled by flotillas of empty landing craft! The secret of military success lies in counter-plotting against the operational plans of your enemy. The way to avoid the Saipan débâcle was therefore to draw the enemy on as far as possible, watch for the time when his assault force was actually in the process of landing, and then launch a concerted, fierce, full-scale counter-attack to annihilate the invading force before it had had time to penetrate beyond the shore-line or establish its bridge-head. The start of this counter-attack was to be held back until word came from the Divisional Commander himself—and these orders were obeyed to the letter by all Japanese forces on the island.

It did not take us long to realise that this stratagem was an utter fiasco. In the first place, the vast flotilla of craft pushing towards the shore like a huge flock of water spiders were no decoys: they were bristling with heavily armed combat troops and as heavily armoured themselves as tanks. And, secondly, the greater part of our heavy fire power— the "crunch" which should have spearheaded our counter-assault—had been neutralised or completely destroyed by the bombardment before it had fired a single shot!

Eventually, waiting in vain for the order from Divisional H.Q., individual units decided to choose their own moment for opening assault on the American forces which had by now succeeded in establishing bridge-heads on the western beaches at two different points. But already the right moment for counter-attack was past.

The attack on us from sea, air and on land continued without respite: every inch of the island seemed either overwhelmed or about to be. Bloody fighting raged over the beaches and in the jungle. But the enemy's strength seemed only to grow the greater. One by one our prepared positions were overrun—and among our soldiers, glancing uneasily from one to another as we retreated into the trees, a feeling grew and grew that we might not after all be going to win. . . . At about 15.00 hours in the afternoon, we got the order to launch an all-out counter-offensive, taking advantage of the poor light after sunset. But somehow the order never took a grip on our troops: it didn't serve to stimulate or to co-ordinate the right kind of spirit. By itself, the order just wasn't enough to allow the counter-attack to be mounted—and in fact it never did take place. Having lost all our prepared positions, we began, bit by bit, to fall back.

At 16.00 hours on July 25th, we were told to prepare for an order to counter-attack with our entire forces at midnight that night. We knew what that meant—the phrase "dying with honour" was to the forefront of everyone's mind. But midnight came and went and the order was never given. "It is still premature for an united counter-offensive: resist stubbornly and work for the piecemeal destruction of the enemy," the message from Headquarters blandly stated.

So it was to be guerilla fighting!

Every unit conducted its operations after that as it pleased. There was a total absence of co-ordination between individual efforts, which were restricted in practice to the night infiltration of the enemy lines, when units would steal up on the American positions and gain small local successes.

Our Section, which had now come under the command of Cadet Asada, was reduced to only thirty men, and our fighting power had reached rock bottom. Rifles and machine guns were not much use for stopping the Australians advancing against us with tanks at their head! However, we had, somehow, to face an attack supported by tanks. Our few remaining sticky bombs comprised the only armoury in any way suited to oppose an assault by tanks and armoured cars. . . .

Throughout August, holed up in our jungle burrows, we waited. The assault did not come until the beginning of

September. We already knew the sticky bombs were virtually useless against American-built tanks—but, as we saw it, the war lasted as long as there was gunfire. As long as we had any weapon at all, we believed, to fight was the only way to stay alive; to leave the line meant certain death. So we fought. As far as the Americans and Australians were concerned, we were just a "mopping up" operation, no doubt. But for us, it was survival or extinction; we would at least give them a run for their money. . . .

With an issue of one bomb per man we stole off into the jungle, watching and waiting for an opportunity to attack an enemy tank. That evening, stalking the noise of moving caterpillar tracks which mingled with the distant roar of shell-fire, we made our way stealthily from pathway to jungle, and then back from jungle to path, eventually groping a route to a plateau from which we could look down on the whole western side of the island. What we saw was like a scene from a nightmare. The entire region had become a withered and barren moor. Here and there an odd coconut palm stood amidst the desolation with all its leaves blown off; like so many blackened and snapped-off telephone poles, they punctuated the ruins. Nothing else remained.

It was then that we heard the sound of a tank. It sounded as though it was climbing up to the plateau from behind us, along the road bordering the spine of the hill. Quick as lightning, we divided into squads and moved down the gentle slopes of the plateau in open order.

There were in fact three tanks, in line ahead. They had the air of marauders returning to base and were taking the incline at a gentle pace. Our squads, ten men strong, closed in to destroy them. My own lot were after the second machine. Just as we were getting near, there was a sudden and unexpected burst of machine gun fire from the leading tank, followed by an outbreak of firing from a small automatic gun. I saw men ahead of us fold up and fall.

The range was ridiculous, but there was only one thing to do. We cut the detonation cap off the bomb and hurled it

23

at the tank. With the sound of gun-fire and explosions in our ears, we turned our backs and made our escape, tumbling down the slope and catching our legs and arms in bush and creeper in our haste to reach the safety of the scrub. Then we made our way cautiously back to the high ground.

When we re-formed in the upper reaches of the jungle, our unit had been reduced to a mere twenty men, still under Cadet Asada.

On another occasion, we attacked tanks with hand grenades. We had been wandering around in the jungle, trying to pinpoint the distant rumble of tracked vehicles, when we saw a number of men walking up the path towards us. With their rolled leggings and twigs tucked into the camouflage netting over their helmets, they certainly looked like "friends". But were they? The rumbling of the tanks came nearer. With bated breath, we decided to stay concealed.

There were four of them, their camouflage carefully contrived to make them look exactly like Japanese. But when they eventually saw us, one of them raised his rifle and fired. They were Australians!

There was a rustling among the leaves as though a wind had suddenly begun to blow as we turned to get away. I pulled the pin of my grenade and flung it at them. Just as I showed them my backside, I heard the explosion. I hadn't time to look behind me again—escape was too important— but there was no sign of an answering burst of fire and nobody pursued us. "Good for you," the Cadet said as I caught up with the remainder of the party—and for the first time I looked back along the path. There wasn't a sign of any of them: all you could hear was the rumbling of the tanks.

5

Stragglers

By the start of October, the only sound we heard was shell-fire so far off that it sounded like distant thunder. But the fighting continued. As I said, the enemy no doubt considered it simply mopping up, but for us it was a full-scale and bloody battle. We had eaten what little there was of our portable battle rations of dried bread, and now we lived on what berries and fruits we could find. We kept up a vain defiance, with nothing left to help us but our grenades. But by now the vital will to fight was absent. Our commanders sent messages advising us to end the senseless resistance, to give up our arms and pack it in. But somehow we didn't. We were afraid to. Afraid that our useless rifles and guns— marked with the noble crest of the Imperial Chrysanthemum—might fall into enemy hands, we buried them deep in the ground. And we prepared, quite resigned, for death as the only possible outcome. For us soldiers of Japan, the only thing left, to our way of thinking, was to deck out our last moments as nobly and bravely as we could.

By now there was no supply base for us to go back to, and we didn't know whether there still existed any Company or Battalion H.Q. where we could have got orders. So we formed sad and sorry little squads—hardly alive, now hiding ourselves away in the jungle, now moving aimlessly along the paths and lanes. We had been reduced to the status of a ragged band of stragglers. Even during this period, however, there were a number of incidents when we tangled with Australian troops backed by tanks, or fell foul of a line of pickets. Fortunately, we always managed to get in our grenades and escape. But on every occasion the number of our already small band would dwindle by the odd one or two. After one such incident, we became separated from Cadet Asada, the man in charge of us. Now, under a Section Leader called Watanabe, we formed a unit of no more than a dozen, just a pitiable gang roaming the jungle in search of food.

There must have been any number of groups like ours in those days, keeping out of the way of enemy patrols and pickets, lurking in or roaming around the jungle. Some were only four or five strong; others numbered as many as fifty or sixty. Such collections tended to drift together through shared anxiety about being chased by the enemy. On the other hand, the larger the group, the greater risk there was of being discovered. So when such a large group *was* attacked, it usually split up again immediately afterwards into the original bands of four or five men. But all the time that we grouped and dispersed, gathered and scattered in this manner, we were held up by our faith that a new and fresh Japanese force would come to relieve us and re-take Guam.

The next thing I remember is being part of a large group of about 150 men. We didn't know the names of each other's units, and we must have been one of the most motley collections of soldiers ever gathered together. But we did have an officer, a big noise from Staff who had once been attached to our Division. His name was Sato.

The existence of such a man, who had for so long been accustomed to off-loading his own troubles and tasks on to others, was hard to bear—particularly by troops who had no longer the will to fight. But we were still alive—if not exactly kicking—and rank and command still counted with us and motivated us. The indoctrination of training is not easily cast aside. Thus it was no more than natural that our activities, grumble though we might, were determined by Sato's orders.

6

Dispersal, Regrouping, Gathering, Scattering

We were making our way down an incline in the jungle, not in any precise or proper formation but proceeding, as it were, piecemeal. Around us the trunks and branches of coconut palms and breadfruit trees, snapped off halfway up by shell-fire or bombs, displayed their hideous, stark remains in the decimated forest. At the command of Sato, we were moving north. Presently we came upon a highway. We realised that it was foolhardy to the point of inviting death to expose ourselves on this open road. Yet unless we crossed it, we could not get to the north. ... And so, urged on by the angry and excited berating of the officer, we stepped on to the macadam.

At once, from the top of an incline above us, there was a burst of gun-fire. In a flash, like grains of rice cast to the winds, our group had scattered in all directions.

"Don't get separated! For God's sake keep together!" I heard Sato screaming. "Keep *together* all of you! Keep together!" The gun-fire continued.

With Watanabe at my side, I once more rushed headlong into the jungle, the two of us scampering like cornered hares. A dozen or more men followed us. But five or six of our own group—I saw when I turned to look—had changed their minds and run back across the road and were making their way towards Sato.

"If any more of you men want to go with him," Watanabe yelled, "then get on with it! Push off quick—but don't forget you'll be with an officer who can't even manage to get his food with his own blasted hands! ... Go on, off with you, double quick!"

The Section Leader paused, panting for breath. "It'll be a dead loss staying with that bastard," he began again, shouting. "Any fool who follows him'll find he's working his backside off like a lackey. But don't let me stop you. Off you go. . . ." He stared after the men on the far side of the road for a moment, gave me a glance, and then turned and plunged back into the jungle.

I followed, but we found we were too weak to go on running for more than fifty yards. The firing had ceased but we could still hear Sato shouting somewhere in the distance.

"I'm not trying to force any of you, you know," Watanabe said when the others had caught up. "Don't do me any favours. You've still got time to go if you want to." He looked round the circle of seven exhausted faces. But not one of us stirred an inch. We never set eyes on Sato or any of his party again.

In fact we didn't set eyes on any Japanese for some time after that. We plunged back into the jungle to the life of a wild animal, roaming aimlessly in search of food. Now and again we did hear rifle-fire, but the shelling seemed to have stopped completely and the mopping up operations appeared to be almost at an end. The patrols did not ease off at all, however.

The seven of us spent our time foraging in the area of Hakoya which had once been our Battalion Headquarters. It was now past the season of the ripening of the breadfruit and, driven by the intolerable emptiness and pain in our stomachs, we took risks we would never have dared to take on other days. Following the course of the river towards the lower ground, we came at last to a military road we had built with our own hands. Numbed to danger by the gnawing within, we hadn't the heart to go back in the jungle. We stayed on the road.

Then suddenly we heard the sound of shell-fire again. It was far away to the north and it hung on the air like a roll of drums. We stopped, scanning the sky behind us.

"So maybe there *is* still fighting going on," Watanabe mused.

"I don't see how there can be," another man answered. "Surely we'd have heard, somehow, if there was? Anyway, those don't sound like our guns to me: they're American tank cannon, I'd say."

"Even so, whether it's our guns or theirs, it does mean that there's some of our people fighting back somewhere, doesn't it?" the Section Leader said.

"Couldn't it simply be manoeuvres or something?" another soldier put in.

"*Manoeuvres?* Oh, come off it!" Watanabe said contemptuously. "Anyway, let's turn towards the north and see what we find...."

I was tying up my bootlace as they turned to tramp back. In my haste I snapped the lace and crouched to join the ends together again.

"Oh, come *on*, Itō," someone said. "You can do that later."

But I thought I might as well finish the job. My fingers, weak from hunger, were clumsy and I took longer than I had meant. I realised that the *zack-zack-zack* of their boots as they marched along the road was gradually getting further and further away. I had finished knotting the lace and was hurrying to thread it through again when there was the sound of a shot and the screech of a bullet from somewhere to my right. Startled, I looked up to see a party of Australians running along a side lane to the right, heading for the junction of this path with the main road along which my party had gone. As I leaped frantically from the roadway into the jungle, I heard a further burst of rifle-fire— from only a few feet away, it seemed. Hardly daring to breathe, I froze like a snake in the thick scrub. There was the confused sound of running feet crossing from my right to my left, then more rifle-fire, this time from fifty or sixty yards to my left. Overlapping the shots came a scream of agony.

My God!—one of our people has bought it! I thought, trying to keep my heartbeats under control. There was silence for a moment, then the blast of a grenade from the heart of the jungle to my left. It sounded about two hundred yards away. After that, the rifle-fire started up again—then I heard American voices calling, quite a way off, it seemed, and they were gradually going further and further away.

After silence had fallen, I still didn't dare to stir. I couldn't for the life of me tell you how long I stayed there: it might have been as little as ten or twenty minutes; it might have been hours. All I knew was that I was alone: there was no hope of finding Watanabe and my Japanese friends again—even if they were still alive. I tried to tell the time by looking at the sun through gaps in the jungle scrub. But the huge leaves of the breadfruit trees hid it from me. I lifted myself up at last, painfully and slowly.

And suddenly I was completely overcome by a hunger so violent and terrible that I could barely manage to stagger two or three paces.

7

Wandering Alone

"I am on my own now," I muttered to myself. And then, without any warning, I was almost carried away by an impulse to scream to the high heavens. But instead of screeching at the top of my voice like a madman, I turned myself around to face the scrub and somehow worked it off on the jungle: I set off as fast as ever I could, which in fact was no better than a crawl down the gentle slope. I had already lost all sense of direction; all I could feel was that savage hunger gnawing away at my belly.

I stuffed into my mouth whatever tree fruits or plant roots I managed to lay my hands on. I don't know what any of them were called. I was quite unable to collect myself and look at things calmly; my thoughts always kept going back to the one point—"Abandoned and all alone, in the end I shall die a miserable death."

"They will be bound to land a further lot of crack, fresh troops to help us out"—the words of Cadet Asada were imprinted clearly on my mind. "So, whatever the outcome, however bad everything may seem, *you must hide yourselves away in the dense tangle of the jungle, and wait for that time to come.* Dying like dogs, with no purpose, is to be regarded as the greatest humiliation by us all. We *must* stay alive—stay alive as long as ever we can and as best we can. And when we know we cannot stay alive and free any longer, we must offer ourselves in sacrifice to our glorious Emperor and the Japan we love. We must do this rather than be forced to face the ignominy of being taken prisoner. You all understand?"

With the thought of these noble words, as the sun set and the light began to fade, I found myself beginning to calm down and grow more at ease. But I still couldn't eradicate this awful sense of isolation and of being entirely on my own. I kept my eyes on the western side of the slope, and when I reached it I hid my body completely, covering myself with jungle scrub, and tried hard to lull myself off to sleep.

The following morning, I woke up to the sound of distant bursts of rifle-fire. That day, I thought, I would climb to the crest of the hill and establish exactly where I was; so I began laboriously climbing up the slope. Whenever I heard gun-fire—I couldn't really judge where it was coming from —I would crouch down, though I didn't for a moment relax my close attention to what I saw about me.

Presently, I came across a small mountain stream. The flow of the water was from my right to my left, and in that I knew I was heading for the west coast, I guessed that this was probably the beginning the River Talofofo. I crossed the stream and began to climb a very steep, wooded incline and then, suddenly and quite unexpectedly, the prospect opened right up. Shell explosions had torn gaping holes in the jungle. I made a detour round this area and then, coming to jungle scrub again, I discovered a group of rocks. At the far end of this rocky strip, I noticed a black shadow that looked at first like a log. I had started to walk up to it before I realised that it was the body of a dead man.

It was an Australian dressed up to look like a Japanese. The body lay prone and spreadeagled, with the head poking into a tangle of scrub. There was camouflage netting on the body, but the branches woven into this netting had withered now; and there were Japanese-type gaiters wound round its legs. I could smell the stench of death, but even so I could not wrench myself away from that dead body. I bent down and turned it face upwards. Its hands were clamped firmly to a rifle. I had a sudden, overwhelming urge to possess this gun. There flashed through my mind a vision of my own light machine gun buried deep in the ground. Perhaps it was my desperate feeling of being alone and abandoned that on the spur of the moment made me demand that rifle. I prised the weapon with its long barrel from the dead man's hands. Blood had clotted and congealed hard all over the butt. Clasping the rifle to me, I made off at top speed back into the jungle. It was a small repeater rifle, and all the bullets were intact!

I went slantways across the slope for two hundred yards or so and hid myself away in the thick scrub. I plucked some wet grass and started to wipe away the blood clots from the rifle—to this extent, at least, it had somehow made me forget my feeling of solitariness.

Why had I taken this rifle? Was it for my own protection? Or had I torn it from the dead man to provide myself with a means of killing anyone who drove me into a corner? Or, again, did I think of it against the time when I should be required to snuff out my own life? Certainly it would enable me to do the deed in due and handsome style. I just couldn't explain my motives to myself: all I knew was that I wanted that rifle—very, very much.

It didn't help the loneliness; but it did strengthen my resolve.

I started again to roam about aimlessly. My movements were like those of a wild animal, driven by hunger. But I did feel that I was moving on the whole in a southerly direction; perhaps it was something to do with the fact that I was wandering in search of a safe hiding place, for I did remember that there were four caves by the upper stream of the river that we used to call the River Tokui. And I still had in my mind a very clear memory of that area.

And, no doubt, another reason was that I felt the place where I was to hide myself away would be that little bit more safe if I were to be familiar with it. But I wasn't able to determine my sense of direction very easily, so day followed day in fruitless wandering. In the meanwhile, I never encountered a single Japanese. Nor, for that matter, did I set eyes on any enemy patrols.

I don't know how many times I must have taken the wrong direction. Even so, I just hadn't the guts to get down towards the low-lying ground and in this way make certain of my position. I dare say that I spent all of two weeks wandering around in this way.

Then early one day I made my mind up and forced myself to try getting down to the low-lying ground. So I made for the main road, which was capable of taking vehicles and which passed through the jungle. I followed this road downhill past a small hill stream and drank a whole skinful of water; then I set off again at an easy pace down the gentle slope of the road, my footsteps making hardly any noise. I have no idea how long I was walking; to judge from the light under the trees, the sun was now well towards sinking in the west.

Suddenly, I heard a rustling sound—as if someone was approaching. Instinctively, I leaped for the thick scrub to my left, and hid myself well away. The rustling sounded as if someone was pushing his way through the scrub. I pointed my rifle towards the road and lay very still, strain-

33

ing all my senses to catch the slightest sound. Presently I heard footsteps approaching along the road that I myself had just walked.

It's sure to be a patrol, I thought. If they discovered me, we'd exchange fire and I'd fight on until they killed me. There were only the footsteps—there was no sound of any talking. I held my breath, like an animal cowering in the path of pursuing huntsmen, and tried to concentrate all my nervous system in my eyes and ears. The steps came nearer and then, dappled in the shadows of the scrub, I could see the feet as they touched the ground with every step. There were four. Four feet—with khaki coloured leggings—passed stealthily by me. Then, presently, I could see the lower halves of two bodies.

"Friends; must be," I thought to myself.

I felt a sudden exultant throb in my breast. But, even now, I did not dare to relax my care; making as little noise as possible, I lifted myself cautiously to my feet and followed them with my eyes. Neither of them had a rifle. "Ah—that means they're Japanese, then," my inner voice told me. I came out into the roadway again just as the two of them entered the scrub to the left. I started after them, my steps anxious and stealthy: the road at this point led down a steep incline. Stalking the swishing sound they made as they pushed their way through the scrub, I once more set off into the jungle at the point where I had lost sight of them. I had gone fifty or sixty paces when I saw them again, halfway up a densely wooded slope. I would have judged the distance at between twenty and thirty yards.

Then, the two of them disappeared, one after the other, for all the world as though they had been somehow sucked into the ground. "A cave, then, surely?" I thought. With never a moment's hesitation, I walked up to the cave—as if I myself were being sucked into it by some hidden power. The cave was overgrown by weeds and scrub but, even so, the mouth was large, about three or four yards high. This black opening led inwards to a silent gloom. With no

34

thought for the consequences, I took two or three paces into the mouth of the cave and called in a low voice:

"Friend or foe? Are you friends?"

There was no reply. I now had no thought for anything other than the impulse to identify them. All caution was thrown to the winds as I repeated my question, advancing step by step into the cave every time I asked it.

"Friend or foe?" I called once more, again in the same low voice.

"Friend," the reply came at last.

As I heard the word I sensed the figure of a man coming towards me through the darkness. Then I was able to make out the face and the body in fair detail; he was quite a tall man.

It was Minakawa Bunzo. The other man was called Miyazawa Tokusaburo, who was in the same trench mortar section as Minakawa. Both of them had been in my Division.

II

THE JUNGLE

1

A Cave Our Hiding Place

There were four caves there, in a row. The one where I had
first joined up with and swopped words with Minakawa and
his friend was the largest of them all. It was four yards high
and led back something like fifteen yards from the mouth;
it was roomy enough for about twenty men to sleep there
without the slightest discomfort. All three of the other caves
in the row were smaller. The third was the next largest and
was linked at its innermost point in a U-shape with the
fourth.

I remembered these caves; remembered our officers talking to each other and one of them saying that it might be
well to make them into the battle command point of
the Battalion. In fact it was this very cave that I had
myself been searching for during my long period of wandering!

We talked together in low voices. I realised that sheer
courtesy demanded that I should give some account of myself, so I told them all the details that I could remember of
what had befallen me since the American landing. I laid
particular stress on the last two weeks that I had spent alone
and isolated, and asked whether we might not, from now
on, move and act, the three of us, together.

"That's quite all right by me," said Minakawa. "What do
you think, Miyazawa?"

"Three's much better than two for keeping spirits up,

isn't it?" Miyazawa chimed in, echoing Minakawa's decision.

These two had been part of a trench mortar section attached to the "Thunder" formation; they told me how they had used up all their shells on the very day of the American assault and how, on the following day, they had taken to the life of the jungle straggler.

The day after our meeting, we decided to move from the large cave to the second largest—this, you remember, was the third in the row, the one linked at its innermost point in a U-shape with the fourth. We had weighed things up and had calculated that the largest cave was nearer to the road, and that therefore the risk of being discovered was higher if we stayed there. "But in the case of this new cave," as I explained it, "we have got our secret passage and a perfect escape route in case of any emergency—so there'd be every chance of coming out of a scrape alive."

Both of them agreed with my suggestions. The entrance to our new cave was narrow and so it was quite ideal as a hidey-hole.

We three found that we were able to live a harmonious life together without any sign of friction. We soon got into the habit of employing the period soon after dawn for our foraging expeditions. At this early stage, we had no means of cooking or preparing food in any way, so our diet consisted almost entirely of raw fruit, roots and berries. The best we could do—and a poor and primitive best it was—in the way of actually preparing food was, now and again, to squeeze a coconut and sip the liquid we got from it; we made believe that this was something like our Japanese bean-paste soup. Looking back on it after the event, and in the light of long experience of life in the jungle, I can see we were pretty green at the time and, to tell the honest truth, we barely stood on the threshold of jungle life.

Before we went out on a foraging expedition, we made it a rule to conceal in a separate place anything that we owned that was conspicuous; in this way we left our hideout as far as possible in a state in which it would not attract undue attention. One such day—when the rainy season had ended and we had had a succession of dry days—we set off first in search of water and climbed to the upper stretches of the stream. As we had still to find a means of storing water, we had to be satisfied with simply drinking our fill on the spot. After this, we entered the jungle forest in search of papaya. We found something that looked worth eating and began to wander around in the vicinity, sampling what we had picked one after the other.

In no time at all we had come out on to the main road. "I am sure there is a coconut grove if we keep carrying on uphill," I said, trying hard to make my memory work.

"It's inviting death to keep on walking up this main road, though..." Minakawa objected.

"But it's so much better to stay on the road; we can climb so much more quickly and save time. So we should have a better return for our labours in the way of a bigger coconut harvest," I rejoined.

While we were discussing which direction to take, all of a sudden, "There's a patrol," said Miyazawa. We leaped to our feet and scrambled back into the jungle. We had no time to take our bearings; we just pushed our way into the scrub, climbing a slope as we went. I caught a glimpse, as it came into my field of vision, of a four or five-man patrol; they looked to me like aboriginals, but I was quite sure they were carrying rifles.

"Recently, aboriginals seem to have been manning patrols in place of American troops," Miyazawa observed.

After this, we made sure of our direction and set off at a slant across the slope. Suddenly, we came upon three men, right in front of us. There was no escaping this time, so I squared up to them. But the middle one of the three spoke —in Japanese.

"What unit are you in?"

"We are from Prosperity," I said, trying to control the quaking of my guts.

41

"Me too. I'm Prosperity, too," he replied. "You looked so scarifying. You had me worried for a moment!"

"Sorry," Minakawa explained. "We almost ran into a patrol of aboriginals a few minutes ago, and we haven't quite got over it yet!"

"You don't think they noticed you, do you?"

"No, they didn't see us. We had got ourselves back into the jungle before they had time. Definitely." Miyazawa spoke with conviction.

"Anyway, they don't appear to be chasing you, do they...?" said one of the others, who was wearing the uniform of a naval rating. I remembered the naval battery which had been stationed near our Divisional Headquarters. I saw that the one in the middle was an army staff clerk, while the third one said that he was a marine engineer.

"We killed a cow this morning you know," said the staff clerk. "We're just cutting it up now."

I had already noticed a queer smell before this, and now I nodded to myself as I realised where it came from. We followed the three of them for about ten yards through the scrub, and there we found a whole cow, its innards all cut away and dressed, placed in a hollow clearing in the scrub. The sailor had an issue knife in his hand and, as he began to slice off the ribs and then the shoulder, he said: "There's so much blasted meat here that, even now there are six of us to eat it, we shan't get anywhere near finishing it."

2

Beef Feast

The shelter that these three had built for themselves was in dense jungle about a hundred yards away. For the whole of the time that the sailor was carving the beef into thin slices, we just could not take our eyes off that knife. Our gaze was glued to every movement of those deft hands. It seemed a veritable age since I had so much as set eyes on a piece of meat, and since this made it sheer agony to restrain the hunger that bit right into my stomach, I walked away from the spot where the sailor was so busy carving and sat myself down in front of the shelter. I couldn't bear to watch him, so I kept my eyes staunchly on the inside of the shelter. They had an untidy stock of utensils and equipment that made me go quite green with envy—there were mess-tins battered almost out of shape, buckets, and I could see even a wash-basin. Behind this pile and further inside the shelter I could just discern something that looked like a Japanese pistol, carefully wrapped in a cloth which only left the top of the muzzle visible.

"Whereabouts are you living then?" asked the staff clerk, who was lying flat on his back two or three yards away from me. I looked round, to find that he had been talking to Miyazawa.

"We are living in a cave in a place we call Tokui," I heard Miyazawa reply.

"A cave?" repeated the staff clerk. "That's taking a hell of a risk, isn't it? For one thing, you can't move it if you want to; and for another, suppose you were discovered; you'd have no way of escape, would you?"

The marine engineer, who seemed to be the leader of the group, turned to speak to the clerk.

"What would you like me to do with the beef? Shall we have it in steaks, or would you rather I made it into some sort of *sukiyaki*?"

"Well, we are giving these chaps a meal as well, so I'd have thought *sukiyaki*'d be the best, wouldn't you? How about it," he asked, turning to us, "could you go for a belly-ful of *sukiyaki*?"

"*Sukiyaki*," Miyazawa replied fervently, "would be absolutely marvellous, thank you ... sir!"

"Right, then. *Sukiyaki*, long time no see: *sukiyaki*, here we come," said our chef, the sailor.

43

He took away a pile of brush-wood which had been so placed as to conceal cleverly an outdoor oven lined with stones. You could just see the red glow of the remains of a fire almost buried in the centre of a heap of ash. I could hardly believe my eyes as I looked at it. "You don't mean to tell us you risk lighting fires do you?" I said to the staff clerk.

"How the hell are we going to make a *sukiyaki* without a fire, you idiot?"

"But how about the patrols if the smoke is spotted?"

"Oh, it's all right when it gets dark, you see. They can't see the smoke then, can they? And don't forget that we are in a jungle hollow here." He half-lifted himself up so that he was sitting directly in front of me, and staring right at me. "You're that scared of patrols, aren't you? After all, they're only a handful of Chamorro tribesmen—that's all. One measly grenade'd settle one of their patrols all right!"

Not one of us three said a word in reply.

A *sukiyaki*, that was to be cooked in boiling water, was already hanging over the fire in a wash basin which did duty for a cooking bowl. Once more I began to feel the pangs of my terrible hunger—so violent that I couldn't see how I could wait for the water to boil and the beef to cook. My gastric juices were beginning to work overtime and I swallowed the saliva that flooded into my mouth as I watched the meat go in.

The *sukiyaki* was nothing more than a very crude boil-up, but it made a really sumptuous feast for us. We just couldn't bring ourselves to lay down our chopsticks (which we had made from thin branches); they never stopped moving—nor, for that matter, did our jaws! In fact I began to get quite an ache in my jaws, and realised how out of practice they were. Our sailor chef kept adding meat and water, one after the other, to the wash bowl, and we were eating so fast and so steadily that there was complete silence —no one's mouth had a space large enough for even the smallest word! There wasn't even time to think how much

44

the dish would have been improved by just a touch of salt.

"What do you say? How about you and us joining forces? After all, six are twice as strong as three are, aren't they?" the staff clerk suggested at last.

We looked at each other, but none of us said a word.

"Whichever way we make it, we are all of us bound to die sooner or later. But before we die, even if there is only one of us, we are going to have a damn good bash at as many of the enemy as possible, aren't we? I think we owe it to our country to steel ourselves to having a fair old go at the Americans. If we do, by our deaths we shall at least accomplish something worthwhile. Now if the six of us form a do-or-die party and make a raid on the American camp, I should say we could strike a pretty fair blow. How do you feel? What do you say to coming in with us and having a crack at them?"

I couldn't believe that the staff clerk really meant what he was saying. After all, how far can you get with a fistful of hand grenades and a solitary pistol? And did he really believe that, while with three you couldn't get anywhere, if only there were six of you, you could make a pact to die fighting gloriously and inflict a fair amount of damage on the enemy? Why couldn't you do this with three men? Provided he worked himself into the right mood, in fact, what was there to prevent just *one* man on his own fighting till he dropped and doing a deal of damage? Now that the party had grown to six, this bloke would no doubt very soon be yapping away saying that, when they got *another* three or four, they really would be in a position to have a fair crack at the enemy! I was pondering over this sort of thing, chewing and munching away on some new slices of meat that had just come to the boil, when I began to feel that I had stuffed my belly far too full. This feeling gradually got worse and worse.

As I listened to the low voice of the staff clerk prattling on and on, I recognised that all the will to fight had completely gone from me. When I was fighting as a soldier among soldiers, and one of a large group, we all believed that, since it was war, it didn't matter when we died. But now it was all different—now that I'd lived through my period of solitary wandering. Whether there were five or ten men, it wouldn't make the slightest difference, and wouldn't retrieve any will to fight in me. I couldn't have survived on my own—that was certain: if I hadn't had the good fortune to meet up with Minakawa and Miyazawa, and if I'd been fated to roam the jungle alone, there is no question but that I'd have bought it sooner or later. If you weren't lucky enough to link up with someone, you couldn't survive.

But then you became exposed to a different danger—once you *had* linked up, the risk grew in proportion to whether the party was two or three or five or six....

The light from the fire flickered across the five faces against the darkening background of the dusk; there was not a sign of the savage look on them that I had noticed during the actual fighting. There just cannot exist, I reflected, a will to fight when there is no fighting power left. Now that our minds were distorted, and we were unable to cut short our lives with our own hands, I realised that the time was gone when we could have carved our way into the enemy's camp.

"With conditions as they are at the moment, I feel that in fact the opposite is the case—the more we increase our numbers, the more difficult it may well become to get things done," said Miyazawa, quietly and thoughtfully. "Suppose we do form ourselves into some sort of volunteer do-or-die group and force our way into the enemy's camp; the greater our number becomes, the greater the hubbub we make, and the more likelihood there is, in addition, of our being discovered by a patrol. That's how I see it, anyway. And if we do end up being discovered before we get any action to our credit, then surely this is to die a dog's death, all to no purpose. Now I don't want you to run away with the idea that, because we've said this, we're afraid to die; but..."

"Yes, that's on the lines of what our battery commander said, you know," I said, gulping down the piece of meat in my mouth. " 'Conceal yourselves in the jungle,' he said, 'and wait for a second landing by a relieving force from Japan. There's sure to be one sooner or later; it will land and retake this island.' That's what he said, and that's what we ought to do—we should keep ourselves alive, whatever the trials and hardships, until that time arrives. That's the time to make our counter-attacks; not before...."

"The battery commander who said that was a fool; and you, too, you're a set of fools for believing such an idiot," said the staff clerk. "Mind you, if you really believe what you've been saying, then I'm the last to try and force any other decision upon you. But there is one thing: think for a minute will you.... It's all very well for savages, maybe—but for human beings like us, forced to learn how to exist as jungle soldiers ... how long in God's name d'you imagine we can survive in this jungle?"

We looked at him and said nothing.

"Suppose we manage, somehow, to keep going until the rainy season next year," he continued. "What's going to happen after the rains begin? We're absolute sitters for some frightful fever, and then we'll die like starving rats with no one to care for us. And even if we escape the fever it's ten to one we'll be discovered by some patrol and end up with a foreign bullet through our brains.... Either way, you see, we end up dead ducks, don't we? And, so far as this second landing by forces from Japan goes, the rescue you're dreaming about may never come. Even if it did, there's no guarantee they'd be able to retake the island, is there? ... Now with all these doubts, isn't it far better, while we still have a little strength and some guts left, for us to have a crack at the enemy—even just one or two of us at a time—and die in a fit of anger and glory? That's what I think, anyway...."

47

Yet one could hardly detect any military fire or martial zeal in his words!

We stayed the night with them in their shelter; they pressed us to do this since we'd eaten far too much meat, really, to want to move very far that night.

We never met up with them again. I can't imagine what became of them—whether they really did make up their minds to carve their way into the enemy's camp, or whether they were taken by the Americans, or whether they met their deaths out in the wilds of the jungle, or whether, finally, they were shot dead by a patrol.

3

The First Move of Hideout

It was Minakawa who was the first to complain of dysentery. We had said our goodbyes and left the shelter with the dawn; we were now out of the jungle and were following the road, keeping a sharp lookout in front and behind, as we hurried back to our own cave. But before we'd been walking for even half an hour, Minakawa was complaining that his stomach felt very, very queer and had crept off into the thick jungle scrub.

"It's dangerous standing around here," I said, glancing backwards and forwards. "Let's go into the jungle ourselves as well."

With Miyazawa, I waited while Minakawa, with some very strange accompanying noises, got rid of just about everything he'd eaten, time after time. And, as I was listening to these strange noises, I myself began to feel a slight ache at the pit of my stomach. Clutching hold of myself, I muttered to Miyazawa, "I feel a bit queer as well, you know."

I went two or three steps into the scrub undergrowth,

48

and brushing away the lower branches, I shoved away the earth to make a hole in the ground and squatted on top of it.

"It looks as if I've got it, too, Itō..." I heard Miyazawa say a few moments later.

"I suppose it's something we've picked up from that beef," I called, almost in a whisper. That was the end of talking for a while. I kept my ears open, but I needn't have bothered; none of us spoke—there was only the noise of our groans of pain as we got rid of all we had eaten.

I realised that we'd done ourselves not the slightest good by eating too much of that *sukiyaki*. Ever since the American forces had begun their landing, we'd had neither the time nor the resources to eat anything that you could call proper food, and we hadn't been able to eat any fish—the fish that we Japanese love. Even though the beef had charmed us completely, we should never have attacked it quite so thoroughly; we should have tempered our greed with caution.

I wonder how many times I had to leave the road and go off into the thick jungle undergrowth before we got back to our cave? Each time I went, I became more uneasy about the way I could feel my strength being sapped so swiftly. But, I suppose, something did come of it—the cautions we gave each other against ever repeating such a foolish blunder. I gave out a tablet of creosote apiece from my secret store. Now and again, we were each of us assailed by a violent pain, and felt that we'd better go out and perform yet once more. On each occasion, we went a considerable distance beyond the cave into the thick undergrowth. Then, just like cats, we took great pains to cover over all the remains, and leave no traces, for there was no telling when the smell of it would be ferreted out by some patrol in the area and would lead the enemy to us. In fact, we never allowed ourselves to be lulled into a sense of security on the grounds that there was no smell from a stool, whether one had diarrhoea or not, and never once during the whole of

49

those sixteen years did we allow this practice to go un-observed.

We each of us distinctly felt this sapping of our energies. Every time I had to go, I fell to thinking that if this dysentery wasn't stopped somehow or other, there'd be no other end to it but death. And I'm sure that the same thought must have occurred to the other two.

I crawled back painfully to our cave after the umpteenth sortie and said, in a low voice, "Minakawa, let's change our hiding-place, shall we? If we were to be discovered in this condition, with our strength so sapped, we shouldn't be able to raise the energy even to get away. But if we moved to a safer place, and were able to get something of a rest-up, I'd say we might well recover more quickly."

"Now, straight away, you mean?"

"Yes. And the sooner the better." I looked from one to the other as I spoke.

"I agree—I've a feeling we've left too many traces of this dysentery about the place. I feel it strongly—don't you?—there's a quite unmistakable stench, what with all this mess that we've left around."

So we busied ourselves as best we could, in our condition, with preparations for the move. By this time, we had got practically nothing in the way of personal effects or household belongings, so the move was a pretty simple one. Off we set in search of the hiding place that met our ideals; we went downhill and towards the south, about 120 or 130 yards from Tokui (where our cave was), and came to a spot in the jungle where not even a wild animal would have been able to pass; and here we decided to build a new hiding place.

We brought a sheet of old Japanese army zinc, which had been jettisoned in the cave, and made it in to something like a roof; then we taxed our ingenuities to find how the trees, as they stood, could be bent and twisted so that they would cunningly overlap it. There was a dense clump of tall undergrowth around this piece of zinc which formed natural walls. And on one side only was there a gap which barely provided a space for us to go in and come out. Even so, there was plenty of space inside this area for the three of us to sleep in complete comfort—about four yards by two-and-a-half yards.

Our site was still near to the Tokui stream; forty or fifty yards or so through the undergrowth, and you could draw water.

Seventy or eighty yards away on the far side of this mountain stream, we found a band of eight men had built a shelter in the undergrowth! It was a few days before we got to know them; but when we did, we discovered that all eight of them were service corps types.

After we'd finished planning and building our shelter, we hadn't even enough energy left to put one foot in front of the other. We laid a floor covering of leaves and grass and flaked out on it, hardly speaking a syllable for hours on end.

It took three days for the dysentery to pass. Then once again, we were assailed by a violent hunger. So we began our new life—roaming the jungle in search of food again.

4

The Revolution in Our Way of Life

Life went on monotonously. To all external appearances at least, once he'd taken part in the search for food, every man was free to spend the rest of his time in lazing around or sleeping as quietly as he could, or in handicrafts, or whatever he wished.

Practically all the military atmosphere that had been there before had now fallen away from us; all sense of rank had disappeared, and we came to feel not the slightest awkwardness in calling each other by such civilian forms of address as Mr. Minakawa or Mr. Miyazawa. A man might have been a corporal or a sergeant, but now, as far as we ourselves were concerned, he became nothing more nor less than a fellow human being. Everything was geared to the single goal of making life more full and complete, so in our choice of words we reverted to the civilian usages of the areas that we came from—"military clothing" became tunic and pants; "long underwear" became simply underwear, and "footwear, within barracks, soldiers for the use of" became again what we'd always called them back home since we were children: sandals.

Sheer existence was at its toughest during the period from November, 1944, to the spring of the following year. Our lace-up boots had by now been reduced to mere tatters, and the uniform and clothing we had been issued with when the unit was first posted to Manchuria had become unwearable, however much you patched and darned.

And in the matter of morale, the one means left to us was to sustain each other by a joint concentration on the single rallying point of the relieving force from Japan; and on the objective of staying alive until that landing force should appear. One felt that once there began to grow any doubts or suspicions about this, then one could no longer survive. . . .

It was the American army's rubbish dump that brought great changes to this way of life of ours—and even provided some luxuries!

Once we had suffered from our violent attack of dysentery, we came to give deep thought and care to what sorts of food we ate. We considered it essential from now on that all water should be boiled and that no food be eaten in its raw state. Our one exception was fruit and berries; these were considered safe when fully ripe. Even so, there was a risk, in the case of papaya or "rose potatoes", of inducing dysentery whenever these were eaten in an over-ripe state. (We gave this name, "rose potato", to a vegetable shaped like a round

52

potato which grew at the root of a prickly scrub plant which looked not unlike a rose bush.)

At the beginning, we learned to make fire from the sun by the use of the lenses of the pocket flashlights we carried. However, in that this method called for the direct light of the sun's rays, it was of no use on rainy days or when the sky was clouded; again, it meant that we could never make fire early in the morning or in the evening after sunset. For pans, we had been using lengths of sheet zinc, but the zinc deteriorated quickly and holes soon appeared in it. Unless we were able to remedy such inconveniences very soon, we realised that we would all end up dying of starvation.

One day, with such thoughts in our minds, we had set out on an expedition with a double purpose—we were both foraging for food and also searching the area around the old Japanese camp for any old refuse which might be made to serve as receptacles or containers, both for carrying and for cooking.

We got on our way and were just about to strike across the road when we heard the faint sound of an engine. Like so many springs recoiling, we leaped back into the undergrowth. We held our breath and, in no time at all, a truck went lumbering past. It took only one glance to realise that the back was piled as high as Fuji with refuse and rubbish.

Now knowing the American camp could not be all that far from where we were, we abandoned our plan to go over the other side of the road, and began our journey back through the jungle to our shelter.

"If we went to search the American rubbish dump, we might well find something of use to us." The suggestion came from Miyazawa.

"But it would be dangerous, surely," I objected.

"If we don't face such dangers, we're going to snuff it, and no mistake. I don't give us more than another six months at this rate." Miyazawa spoke with a deal of seriousness.

Just then, we heard the sound of the truck once more. It

came up at a furious speed and passed us by, no more than thirty or forty yards in front of us. It was about a quarter of an hour later that we came upon the American rubbish dump. It was in sunken ground, a little distance into the undergrowth from the road. But we didn't do anything as rash as go up close to it at once.

"There's no saying that the truck won't be back again," warned Miyazawa, who was always one for caution.

We knew that it was a fair distance from this point to the American camp on the coast, but we calculated that the journey could be done in five or six minutes in a truck of this kind. There wouldn't be time to prospect the place properly, in fact, before there was a risk that the truck might return.

"There's nothing for it but to wait till it gets dark," said Minakawa.

You could see the dump, so near, only just across that damned road. So near and yet... We retraced our steps, having decided that we would return to the dump that night. It had everything you could hope for. We began a scavenging "ferry" service which continued night after night.

With every day the dump brought new improvements to our living conditions. We used empty tins and cans to make pans, and we also devised tanks for water storage, which held about four gallons. We made sewing needles out of bed springs and learned how to pick a piece of material to pieces, join the strands, and make a length of thread that was strong and durable. And we made ourselves rucksacks out of sheets of tenting. From this time also we learned how to make ourselves shirts and trousers or shorts by piecing together cast-off garments.

"If they throw out things as fine as this, they must be living in sheer bloody luxury," we thought, recalling the life of pinching and scraping we had suffered under the Japanese army. And, whiling away our leisure, we got so engrossed in clothes-making that time seemed to pass very quickly. On one occasion, we picked up a heavy calibre shell-case. "It's a naval shell-case, no doubt," we said to each other. It was a round case, just over a yard long and about one foot in diameter. It was made of light aluminium, lined on the inside with brass plating, and there was a layer of rubber packing still attached. It certainly made a wonderful piece of equipment and we put it to a variety of uses; its first function was a food preserver, and later we employed it as a storage place both for meat preserved with salt and for dried breadfruit. And the rubber packing made it possible for the shell-case to be hermetically sealed. There was something else we picked up in that rubbish dump—something that was absolutely essential to life in the jungle—a "woodman's hatchet". It was about one foot, four inches in length, the blade being about ten inches across, and the depth just over four inches. The edge of the blade turned up almost to form a circle and, with a rasp that we had also picked up, we sharpened the tip of the hatchet and used it as we would use a kitchen knife back home in Japan. We used this "barbarian chopper" for cutting wood and for all kinds of similar purposes; it always hung from a belt around the waist of one of us, tucked in a sort of sheath which we had made by binding with leather thongs a couple of shavings of wood. We also found a knife which we could use for dressing food; it was much narrower than the other, and these two were kept in the one sheath, always at our waist ready for use in any and every circumstance. We concocted a cutthroat razor out of a piece of stainless steel, so that we always had a remedy when our beards grew too long. But none of these vital implements and utensils was ever stored in our shelter—or if it was, only on exceptional occasions; it was our normal and regular practice to insist on concealing such valuable possessions in one of the caves about a hundred yards away. Our motive in doing this was to make it a simple matter for us to escape unimpeded by such belongings in the case of unexpected attack by an enemy patrol or by aboriginals. Again, in such a case, after we'd made good our escape, when it came to constructing a new shelter, such implements could easily be brought into use again after a simple visit to their hiding place, whereas we dare not revisit a shelter once it had been discovered. In this matter we were helped considerably by the terrain, for there were innumerable small openings and caves in the many rock-formations in the jungle, and among them no small number that would never be discovered even by the aboriginals who knew the ground well.

5

The Parting With Minakawa

In May of 1945, we faced our second rainy season since the landing. This period was by far the most difficult of all for us in the matter of food, for we had run out of "rose potatoes" and it was still far too early for the breadfruits we ate in their place to ripen. We had not yet by this time mastered the arts of food preservation so, for quite a number of days running, we suffered from desperate hunger. Nor did the squalls, which attacked us Heaven knows how many times in the day, help to make our lives any the less wretched. We cowered in our shelter, but, even so, huge raindrops were driven in on us by the violent winds and struck us slantwise. All three of us found it disagreeable to talk and remained sullenly silent. And it was just at this juncture that I proposed we rebuilt our shelter. However, there was a difference of opinion here between Minakawa and myself, and neither of us would budge or give way in the least. The bone of contention was that whereas I proposed we should make the overall dimensions of the shelter *smaller*, no more than two-and-a-half yards square, and that we should use the overlap of zinc sheeting saved by this contraction to give us further protection from the rain, Minakawa suggested that the rain could not be driven in on us by the wind if we made the roof a good deal lower than it was at the moment. Other points on which we differed were the positioning of the entrance, and even that of the fireplace! It didn't get as far as exchanging blows, but we did exchange words, so often and so bitterly that it looked as if the dispute would go on and on without ever reaching a solution.

"I agree with Itō's idea," Miyazawa said, hugging one knee between his arms and crossing it over the other. "However low we decide to make the roof, I'm sure we'll still get drenched just the same."

"No. If you make the place any more confined than it is now, it will be far too close and stifling for us to be able to get any proper sleep," Minakawa objected.

"But if we made it so that the roof could easily be detached once a squall had blown over...?" Miyazawa countered.

"Rubbish! It'd be nothing more than a waste of precious energy. I simply couldn't stand living in a place as poky as that; I couldn't bring myself to ... in fact if you insist on building it that way in the face of my objections, then I'll leave.... Yes, I'll quit and go somewhere else," Minakawa said pettishly, working himself up into a fine rage. "Oh, you want to be alone, do you?" I snarled, feeling ridiculously like a cross-questioning lawyer in court. "Yes I do. I'll get that party of eight to take me in with *them*," Minakawa said illogically. We were both pretty worked up by then. Such trivialities can assume gigantic proportions under conditions of hardship. I was in no mood to hold out the olive branch—and even if I had, Minakawa was unlikely for the moment to take back what he had said and stay with us. Scowling, he stuffed his belongings in a rucksack—if you could call it that—which he had made from a tarpaulin we'd found at the dump, and stalked off through the rain with an air of pride and triumph in his bearing.... Miyazawa, like me, made not the slightest attempt to dissuade him. After a

57

short while, I began to feel a remorse that weighed heavily on me, for my obstinacy and my hasty temper. But it was not long before the other side of me, the positive and active part of me, won the day and I had soon forgotten this weight on my mind. No doubt Minakawa, for his part too, after the madness of a momentary fit of anger, was regretting our senseless squabble. However, as long as he did have other chaps around him, it wouldn't mean that his leaving us would lead on his part to a sense of unbearable and desperate isolation. In fact, before very long, we got into the way of visiting each other in our respective homes and giving each other meals from what few rarities or delicacies we had managed to lay hands on.

The next event I remember took place on July 12th, judging by an entry I made in my diary. After Minakawa had left us, we had in fact rebuilt our shelter so that the inside measured two-and-a-half yards square—which was ample for us both to lie down in comfort, and yet not feel that there was so much spare space that we were isolated or distant from one another. Actually, although Minakawa and Miyazawa came from the same part of Japan—the district of Niigata, on the north coast of the main island—they had not come to know each other until the time of the fighting and our recent period of jungle-bashing. Even so, in a way, I was quite gratified when Miyazawa did me the honour of opting to stay behind with me. And I made a very solemn promise to myself that I'd never quarrel with anyone ever again, and strove my very best to keep to this promise. The two of us came to create between each other a much greater intimacy and joint understanding than could ever have been (or was in fact) the case while we were three. Never once was there any opposition of views or ideas between us— whether we were cooking or preparing food, or foraging, or whatever.

That morning, as usual, I woke up before it was light. I felt terribly heavy and languid.

"Have you noticed, Itō,"—apparently Miyazawa was

58

awake too, for there he was talking to me—"there's no sign of the usual squall yet? Maybe it's blowing itself out up on Mount Honda."

"M'm. Yes," I muttered, nodding vaguely; I hardly took in what he was saying, because my thoughts were playing on something entirely different.

"We've not been over by Mount Honda for some time, have we?" Miyazawa prattled on, not realising that I couldn't have cared less about what he was saying. "We ought to be going pretty soon in case the breadfruit is ready for cropping." I voiced my thoughts, ignoring his questions. "Had you realised—it's the festival of *Bon* back home today," I muttered miserably. "We still use the old calendar in my village, so I suppose the real date should be sometime next month. Even so..." "Oh. It's July 12th, then—or should be." Miyazawa suddenly became as downcast as myself. "We also keep *Bon* by the old date at home, though in the town some districts use the new...." He raised himself up on one elbow and burst out: "Oh, good grief, who were the swine who began this beastly war? Let them fight it themselves, I say, and leave us ordinary people to go home and enjoy our *Bon* in peace...." He was almost in tears. By now it was quite light. "If only you can manage to stay alive," I soothed, sorry that I had started him off on this tack, "the time'll come when you *will* be able to dance the *Bon* again; I'm sure it will. It must do." I spoke in the low voice we customarily used in the jungle—as much to convince myself as to help Miyazawa. But he seized eagerly on my words. "Yes, yes, you're right, Itō," he exclaimed. "It has to be like that. But the first and most important worry we have—as I was saying earlier—is food.... And talking of food, don't you feel we should be on our way? We should have begun our foraging long ago. How about it?"

I nodded and pushed myself into a sitting position, pulling on my home-made sandals and beginning to lace them up. The previous night, I had left them by my feet when I lay down to sleep. My hand-made socks were already on—I

59

never removed them, even for the shortest period. For one thing, this was a fair precaution, I thought, against any injury to my feet in case of an emergency when we might have to make a dash for it; and for another, these socks were an essential protection against having my feet rubbed sore by the thongs of the sandals—which I had made myself by stringing together thin strands of wire.

The sandals themselves were made from the tyres of an abandoned American car. They were cut from the rubber in a shape and size much larger than the actual measurements of my feet. This again was for several reasons: first, and by far the most important, it was to prevent us leaving any marks that could be readily identified as footprints; secondly, so that these sandals would kill the sound of our footsteps as we walked; and, thirdly, so that we would not suffer any injury to the soles of our feet when we walked either in the jungle or on the rock-formations.

It happened just as I stepped out of our shelter, a pace behind Miyazawa. From behind the stream, there came the sputter of gunfire, followed at once by the loud, rending explosion of something like a hand grenade.

With an immediate reflex action, we hurled ourselves back into our shelter and grabbed up the rucksacks we'd been using during the night as pillows.

"It's over by the shelter that Minakawa and his group are living in," I said, looking round at Miyazawa.

He had also got his rucksack slung over his shoulder by now, and together we made a dash for it into the dense jungle to our left. As we ran, a second burst of gun-fire started up, followed by three or four big explosions. We kept on running, to get as far away as possible.

"Mind you don't step on any branches and snap them...." I panted.

"I'm all right, Miyazawa replied from behind me. "It's you, you great fat podge, that should be watching it!"

We'd gone about three hundred yards before we thought it safe to stop. There was no more firing or explosions. But from where we were, encircled by tall scrub, we couldn't see a thing.

"Let's climb a tree and see if we can spot anything," suggested Miyazawa.

We shinned up a breadfruit tree just at the side of us and looked out.

There was a column of white smoke hanging above the thick jungle some distance away to our right. This put it beyond all doubt that the raid had been on the shelter of the party of eight who had taken in Minakawa. From our hidden observation tower among the dense foliage of the tall tree, we could not take our gaze from the sinister cloud which floated sluggishly over the tips of the forest branches.

"Our shelter's sure to be discovered, too," muttered Miyazawa in a broody tone. "They've only to go across the stream and it's not difficult to find."

I nodded in silence. My mind was full of Minakawa. I thought back to Minakawa at the point when he abandoned our shelter. If only I'd agreed with his ideas, it would never have come to this. The thought started to seep into my mind and spread like sour water.

"I wonder if Minakawa was clever enough to get away?" I asked, biting my lip.

"There's precious little hope," answered Miyazawa. "There was some pretty heavy shooting going on, you know. It sounded to me as though there were about ten people firing ... no, with that to cope with, he can't have had much chance."

"And with nine of them living together, there was a pretty fair risk of their being discovered. What with all the comings and goings, they're bound to have left traces of themselves."

Presently the smoke disappeared completely. But, like cats chased up a tree by a dog, we could not bring ourselves to come down. The dense jungle had now become completely still again, almost as if it were dead; the occasional cry of a bird whose name I did not know was the only sound that broke the silence. "It looks as if nothing's happened to our shelter after all then, doesn't it?" I heard Miyazawa mutter.

I nodded again. It was their practice, whenever they found any of our shelters, to burn them to the ground. So if we saw smoke rising from that area a second time, we could take this as evidence that our own shelter had also been discovered. It wasn't that we stayed up the tree waiting for, or even expecting, this to happen; it was rather that we couldn't bring ourselves to come *down*. In fact, one felt rather as if a large-scale hunt were going on, and that one was part of it—the quarry!

However, this was something of a misconception on our part, for there was not the slightest sound, either of human voices or of rifle fire or of dogs barking. I felt a numbness beginning to spread right through my body. I could tell from the state of the sun that it was not very far from noon.

Not long afterwards, clouds started to blow up and cover the sun and huge raindrops began to fall. Absolutely dripping, wet through, and still clinging to the thick trunk, we must have looked for all the world like two protuberances on the tree! For we still could not bring ourselves to make the slightest movement. The squall swept through the leaves and swayed the trees like a typhoon; only after it had passed, when the dripping of the raindrops from the leaves above us had at last almost stopped, did we begin to move down from our refuge.

It was good to feel the earth under our feet again— sodden though it was—but we found it hard to keep a foothold with our hand-made sandals. "Why don't we try going back to our hut...?" Miyazawa asked in an undertone.

"It's risky, you know. If we go back now, they might still be hiding up in wait for us. And even if they're not waiting for us, you can't tell that we mightn't bump into them somewhere. No, I think it would be safest not to go near our shelter until tomorrow morning," I objected, putting my lips close to Miyazawa's ear. And I must have convinced

62

him, for he didn't try any more to force his opinion on me. Choosing the sunset as the time to move, we decided to hide up for the night in the cave by the Tokui where we'd lived earlier. We chose the one with the U-shape at its innermost point. Here we had hidden certain possessions which were not so much necessary for survival as precious for sentimental reasons and therefore things which we would on no account wish to be lost (these included spare shirts and trousers, the shell-case, and the repeater rifle). To our great relief and joy, there they were, all neat and tidy, with not the slightest sign of interference by anyone.

That night, neither of us was able to sleep well. You'd just gone off into a doze when you were wide awake again, and once you awoke, something made you start talking about Minakawa and the rest of the group he had joined. Both of us were convinced that all nine of them must have been shot to death and their shelter completely destroyed.

6

Minakawa Still Alive

Next morning before it was light, wearing light clothing only, we approached the shelter by the bank of the river. There wasn't a sound to be heard. But we couldn't get rid of the nagging feeling that somewhere in the vicinity the aboriginals had their rifles cocked ready and trained on us.

We stopped for a moment at a point a mere five or six yards from the shelter. This was to strain our eyes and ears for any and every hint as to the condition in which we would find it. There was not the slightest indication that anyone was there. Already, the eastern sky had taken on the colours of the dawn. I exchanged glances with Miyazawa and began to walk.

63

The shelter was still there—just as we had left it, with not a single thing touched or altered.

"They didn't find it after all...." I whispered. We went into the shelter, which was dripping wet, and collapsed wearily on the floor. Lying flaked-out on my back, I turned my head to look at Miyazawa and said:

"It's no longer safe here either, I suppose.... There'll be a patrol doing another hill-sweep around here again today, and that's for sure. What do you say, Miyazawa—let's start right now to look for a new hiding place and move our stuff as soon as we've found somewhere?"

"No. What I say is that it would be safer to stay put. The more we move, the more risks we run," Miyazawa objected. "If we weren't detected yesterday with all that fuss and rumpus going on, then I think we're past the danger point and will be quite safe from now on."

"But if they've started on a real, thorough combing out of us jungle stragglers, then they could well come back to this area again today!"

"No. Never. I tell you, for a day or two, if no longer, we're in the safest possible place here.... Even if they *have* started a systematic hunt—and I don't for a minute think you're right—after they'd spent all day yesterday around here, they'd have reported 'search completed' as far as this area's concerned. There's no two ways about it—I'd bet my right arm on it. They'll be figuring that any jungle stragglers left in this area will have been so scared that they'll have taken themselves off as far as their quaking legs can carry them."

"I suppose you may be right, but ..." I was still only half-convinced, still inclined to doubt. "I think we'd best get away from this shelter for the next two or three days—in the daytime, anyway. But after that, say after three days, if there's been no signs of them, then I suppose it'd be safe to settle down here again."

"I don't think you ought to be as scared as you are," said Miyazawa—in a tone which sounded as though he'd be prepared to make concessions. "Maybe there's no harm in being over-cautious, however—so for two or three days, perhaps, as you say..."

Once he'd made this concession, we both of us got away from the shelter immediately.

During the daytime we roamed the jungle, only going back after it had got dark. Neither that day nor the following day did we discover anything out of the ordinary.

"It's beginning to look as if my theories were right, after all," Miyazawa said.

"M'm. But today's only the second day, remember. If all goes well tomorrow, then, as you suggest, we'll settle down again here for the time being," I replied. It wasn't so much that I felt uneasy any more; it was rather a case of my finding it hard to swallow my pride.

At dawn on the morning of the third day, with the sky turning a sort of sparrow-coloured grey, we made our preparation to leave the shelter, having agreed that this was for the last time.

It was just as I had finished fastening my sandal straps. I heard a noise as if someone was brushing past leaves, and I was sure that Miyazawa, keyed-up as he was for the slightest noise, must have sensed it too. Together we leapt out of the shelter and hurled ourselves in the jungle.

"Itō!" I was certain my name was being called. Then I heard the sound of a tongue clicking. I exchanged looks with Miyazawa.

"Itō! Miyazawa! It's me!" I heard the faint voice again.

"It's Minakawa, I think!" murmured Miyazawa.

Heaving a great sigh of relief I made my way cautiously through the thick tangle and looked between the leaves towards our shelter. There were two men standing by the doorway. Beyond all doubt, one of them—his profile was silhouetted and I got a good look at it—was Minakawa....
We leapt out of the jungle and rushed up to him.

"Mi-na-ka-wa"—I could barely get my mouth to work and I could not stop myself from shuddering and shaking.

65

"We were quite certain you'd bought it..." said Miyazawa. "Oh, how wonderful! What a miracle!"

"M'm. It looks as though the rest of them bought it, though...." Minakawa's voice was quiet and controlled. "We thought we'd try coming to contact you here—we came yesterday, and the day before as well; but no trace of you; and not even any signs that you'd lit a fire...."

"That's because we only came back at nights to sleep," said Miyazawa. "It was Itō's idea—he said we'd be safe that way. But how marvellous to see you alive and kicking...!"

We walked across to the shelter where Minakawa and his group had been living: it lay just over five hundred yards from the site of our own shelter. It was a small hiding place, built on to and utilising a cave in the rock face.

The attack had come from a squad of aboriginals of the Chamorro tribe. It seems as though, from about the beginning of 1945, that they had taken over patrol duties from the American forces and begun a systematic hunt for stragglers from the Japanese army. What with their ill-feeling towards the Japanese and the fact that they knew the ground, they were far, far more formidable than any American or Australian. They used dogs, and if they recognised you for a Japanese they'd open fire without giving you the slightest chance. And they were past masters in the art of moving silently; without the slightest sound, they'd be right on top of you, fling their grenades and follow up with a burst of rifle-fire just to make sure the job was properly done.

Minakawa said he had no idea how many aboriginals there had been in the group that had attacked their hiding place. But they were in semi-circle formation and they had come in very rapidly to the attack. From a bare six or seven yards' distance through the thick jungle they had pumped bullets at the shelter and followed this rifle-fire with a rain of grenades. Luckily for Minakawa, he was just making ready to go out on his own and he was at the far side of the shelter from the point where the attack was made. The

66

aboriginals' rifles were taking aim when he sensed that something was wrong; the firing had already started, and he heard someone shrieking as he leaped for the scrub with a shout of surprise. Next, he heard the explosions of the grenades—but by then, panic-stricken, he'd covered a good two or three hundred yards.

"Happily for me, the jungle there was as thick as I could ever have hoped for. You could hardly see your hand in front of you, it was so dense. So I hid up there, just where I stopped running. Then this other chap, Umino, came past. So I called him in to my hiding place and we lay up there till well after noon."

"And the other seven? What became of them?"

"They all bought it..." Umino put in, spitting out the words.

Minakawa, by contrast, spoke thoughtfully and with restraint. "We went very early yesterday morning to look at the burnt-out remains; we didn't come across anything like a dead body, but we did see traces of what looked like freshly dug graves."

"If they *are* still alive, we're bound to meet up with them somewhere, sooner or later," Umino commented sourly.

I remember Umino's face well. Always that same ill-humoured and sullen look, and always lazing around, as if he could flake out any minute.

We were not disturbed by any more gun-fire after that, and presently we were into another dry season. Minakawa and Umino visited our shelter now and again and usually, on such occasions, we talked the whole night through—conversing quietly about such things as our home-towns, the war, food and—of course!—women. And you could sense from these conversations that, deep down in our hearts, all our hearts, we still believed there *would* be a counter-attack and a second landing by a relieving force from Japan. At such times, Minakawa would nearly always go off on his own, sit himself down outside our shelter, and gaze at the moon and the stars.

7

The Festival Feast and Its Aftermath

I suppose it takes several hundred generations before an animal's habits become instinctive. And, similarly, it took a long time for us to accept strain in face of an external enemy as one of *our* habits, something that we found we could live with. I suppose it would also require any number of generations—and not only this but one's whole birth and breeding too—for one not to feel the tension *as* tension. Nevertheless, although by this time we had not yet reached a point of being able to regard our shelter as a place where we were within the "dead area" as far as the enemy was concerned, at least, in that we hadn't heard a single shot for ages and had not set eyes on a single outsider, there was no doubt that there did occur a gradual and unconscious slackening of the tension.

We found it quite impossible to discover any joy in anything other than food: so seventh heaven for us consisted, after all, in sticking our teeth into something that was both tasty and of high nutritive value.

We were into our third dry season since the defeat of the Japanese forces; it was one of the worst possible times for us, this tiding over the between-season when we were on the point of switching to "rose potatoes" from our staple food, breadfruit.

I still remember the entry I made for November 25th in the first diary I kept—which I was later to lose; it read something like: "Clear weather; celebrated the Festival of Emperor Taishō with a meal of beef." I had wasted quite half the day in a fruitless hunt after a stag. Carrying the repeater rifle that I still kept hidden in the cave, I had chased the beast from jungle to valley and from valley to rocky hillside, but the only thing I got to show for my pains was one of the wretched animal's antlers!

"Oh! What the hell's the use? We'll have to pick a few potatoes and satisfy ourselves with those..." I said to Miyazawa.

"And there we were thinking we'd have a real good feast of venison to celebrate the Festival of Emperor Taishō,"— Miyazawa's words echoed my thoughts. "Can you make do with frogs?"

The frogs on Guam were like slightly smaller versions of the toads we know in Japan; though even these were by no means easy to find at this particular season. But they were our most regular and favourite subsidiary diet. These frogs were said to carry poison under the ears, so the only sections we thought it safe to eat were the thick thigh areas. They tasted pretty wishy-washy and you'd never in your wildest moment call them tasty; however, roasted on an iron plate, they did make a substitute that you could just about bear to eat.

We hid the rifle away in the cave and got back to our shelter while it was still light. We came out of the thick scrub at the front of our shelter to find Minakawa and Umino squatting there waiting for us.

"Any spoils?" There was a pleasant and joyful tone, unusual for Minakawa, in his question.

"Nothing but a measly frog or two," I replied.

"Well, frogs'll have to do us, then, won't they?" There was hidden amusement in Umino's words. "But don't worry. For, this time, we've brought with us the absolute tops in eats!"

"What the devil do you mean—the absolute tops?" asked Miyazawa.

Minakawa lifted himself up slowly, poked his arm into the scrub, and produced an enormous hunk of meat. It took only the swiftest of glances to realise that it was beef; a lovely hunk of beef, under our very eyes, freshly cut into three or four large pieces!

69

"How on earth did you lay your hands on that?" As I spoke, my eyes wide open in amazement, I looked from Minakawa to Umino.

"We decided today that we'd extend our activities a bit further to the north. You see, I'd remembered that, in the north, there's quite a lot of stock-breeding by the aboriginals. So I was wondering whether something ... well, you know what I mean, don't you?" Umino said. "I moved stealthily and got very close to one of their animals. I was thinking that, if I could get close enough to bash in its head with my shovel ... and then suddenly there it was coming right towards me! Maybe it was reared domestically—and maybe this had something to do with its being quite tame and friendly. Anyway, the thing more or less gave itself up; it came straight towards us, its nose pointing right at us, as if it were saying, 'Come on. Here I am ready for the slaughter!' As it's the Festival of Emperor Taishō, it could hardly have been better timed for our celebrations! After all, if you've got damn-all to eat, you can't do much celebrating can you? ... I said to Minakawa that we'd invite you over to our hiding place so that we could all celebrate together. But Minakawa said our shelter was a bit too small and he suggested we'd do far better to have a leisurely and spacious celebration in your place. So here we are—beef and all."

After Umino had given us this rather unnecessarily lengthy explanation—in his own broad, dour and inimitable dialect—we discussed how we should cook the meat. On no account could we bring ourselves to eat another meal of boiled beef! So, in the end, we decided to remove all the fat and cook the beef as a fry with this fat. And once we'd made our minds up, we divided out the work between us and busied ourselves in preparation for an evening meal the like of which we'd never tasted since we took to the jungle.

By now, we had got quite used to making fire. We had remembered how we'd seen the aboriginals light their tobacco by rubbing together strips of bamboo, and in the first place we had tried to copy this method; finding, in fact, that it was by no means easy. So we evolved our own method—which involved wire rope which we had picked up in the American dump. We wound it round a log and rubbed it vigorously until it became very hot. Then we used some gunpowder from old bullets we'd picked up on the site of the Japanese army camp—either sprinkling the slightest trace of powder over the rope or pressing the hot wire into the powder; either way, the powder would always sputter and flare up. We found this method never failed and we soon became experts at catching the exact moment when the powder flared and transferring the flame to thin pine-wood spills as slender as a tooth-pick. The flame was then transferred to charcoal cinders—and there was a cooking-fire!

During the dry season we were able to gather any amount of dry grasses and sticks, so we found very little difficulty in our attempts to reduce as far as possible the amount of smoke that came from our fires.

While Miyazawa and Umino were busy making the fire, Minakawa and I first cut away the fat and then put it into the empty tin we were to use as a pan. The fat crackled noisily over the flames and soon started to melt. Although we called it a "deep fry", we had no batter for coating, and all we could do under the circumstances was cut the beef into pieces of a suitable size (fit for eating at a single mouthful) and drop these into the boiling fat one by one—rather like a Swiss *fondue*.

"I think we'd better add them a little more slowly. It's making far too much noise, don't you think?" There was a deal of anxiety in my words. But nobody took the slightest notice of me. Perhaps it was the luscious smell of the fat that had caused something of a numbness in our responses; any-way, our minds were entirely absorbed in the single matter of eating! The fried beef fritters, fished from the pan with a home-made wooden sieve, were conveyed swiftly to our

71

mouths with wooden chopsticks. For a dressing, we used a wild red-pepper. We smacked our lips so much at our Festival banquet that we even forgot about eating breadfruit!

"God! I just can't manage another mouthful...." It was Umino who was the first to complain of a feeling of satisfaction.

In restrained voices we talked together about the war, our jaws still plugging away steadily at the fritters. Our stomachs were filled to the brim—but our tongues and our throats refused to admit satisfaction yet. However, the limit was eventually reached, and then, with no mind for tidying up, we simply lay down in line inside our shelter, relishing the long-forgotten feeling of well-being and satisfaction that comes from a full—even an over-full—stomach.

There was still more than two-thirds of the meat left.

The next morning, the four of us again ate the beef "fry" to our fill, and even then, there was more than half of it left at the end of our meal.

"Let's go shares on the rest of the meat," suggested Minakawa.

So Minakawa and Umino wrapped their half in an old, tattered piece of cloth and set off back to their own shelter.

Beef was a thing of real value in our eyes; if it had been at all possible, we would have liked somehow to have preserved what we had left. But we had still not learned how to obtain salt as early as this—the main drawback being that it demanded a great show of courage to go down to the shore and collect water from the sea. The route required one to traverse the road used by American service vehicles, and from the point where one crossed this road to the shore there was a further walk of at least a mile.

"It might well keep if we do it up in fat," Miyazawa suggested. I, too, was attracted by this idea.

The fat was not quite cold yet, so Miyazawa raked and gathered the embers, fed them expertly with some new, dry twigs and soon had the fire going again as merrily as ever. In the meantime, squatting on my knees, I began to cut the

72

meat into pieces convenient to handle: and in that there was, I suppose, well over half a stone still left, it took a deal of time and hard labour before I seemed to be making any impression on it. As I cut the slices, Miyazawa took them and placed them in the pan and, for the whole of the time he was thus working and moving industriously, he kept up a constant jabber. He was obviously in the best and happiest of moods, chattering away about his experiences while he was wandering in the jungle with Minakawa and ate in its raw state beef that was crawling all over with maggots; or what a tasty dish you could make out of an ox penis! The meal, and now the work, really had loosened his tongue!

I was still cutting the raw meat—with a small, edged tool that we'd made out of stainless steel. Standing over me and looking down at my face, Miyazawa said, "How about it? Have one of them!" But I just couldn't eat anything more, so I shook my head.

Just then, I heard a noise. It was of a quite different kind from the sound of the meat crackling in the hot fat; it was much more like the noise made when a twig is snapped. With a start, I lifted my gaze.

And just at that second there was the crack of a gun-shot from the jungle to the right of me. I can't remember now; maybe it would be more correct to say, not that I heard the report but that I *saw* the belch of fire from the gun barrel; certainly, in that instant, I saw the face of the aboriginal who was pointing his rifle straight at us. There was something like five or six yards' distance between us, I suppose; but it felt to me like a mere couple of yards. I couldn't tell you whether it was as I heard the report of the gun that I shouted and flung my body round instinctively, or whether I had heard the shot before I shouted and moved. I have the impression, too, that I heard Miyazawa shriek; however, by that time, I was scrambling desperately through the scrub like a wild animal, crawling, thrusting, running, in no fixed direction. Getting away, that was all that mattered. I didn't

73

feel any fear; it was surprise rather than fear that snapped on the power that fed my limbs in that scramble to escape into the jungle.

I fled deep into the heart of the forest. And oddly, once I realised that there wasn't a sign that I was being pursued, fear began to assail me. I found I was unable to walk; and I had no idea how far I had run.

It was at this point that I noticed how silent and still it was in the forest; it was as if everything were dead. I cowered in the middle of a dense tangle of scrub. Time passed me by—I lost all sense of how long I had been crouching there.

There was no more gun-fire—but I remained there, un-moving and still as a stone. I began to think about Miya-zawa. Surely he could not have been killed? I tried to per-suade myself that the shriek had come from my own throat rather than from his, and that when he had appeared to topple, what had happened in fact was that, like me, he was hurling himself into the jungle. And it was while I was in this way picturing what might have befallen Miyazawa that I became aware of myself, concentrating every nerve in my body on the noises around me.

I wonder how many hours it took for me to bring myself to stir? For a long time, I couldn't even raise enough resolve to determine where I was. But when I did presently recover myself, I realised that I was barely two hundred yards from our shelter. There was still not the slightest sound—either of aboriginals or their dogs. So, little by little, I edged my way in the direction of our home.

There was no hint of any smell that might have told me the shelter had been burned down. And, looking back on it, I realise that it was only after I knew it had not been fired that I summoned enough resolve to see what had happened to Miyazawa. With only about fifty yards to go, I stopped once more. From the light and the position of the sun, I knew it must now be well on in the afternoon. I heard a faint scampering sound and started—but before I had time

74

to swing round, my experience told me that it was only a wood mouse. Making not the slightest sound myself, I inched gradually along the remainder of the route. As I neared the shelter, my nose did pick up a smell—the pungent aroma of burned fat!

I could have screamed aloud with rage at our idiocy. After all our precautions over all those months, we had allowed our greed to overrule our good sense: it was the smell of cooking that had drawn the aboriginal to our retreat....

Miyazawa had been killed outright by that one shot. He lay spreadeagled, just as the bullet had felled him, his feet facing the cooking pan that had caused his death, the upper half of his body submerged in the scrub. A piece of cloth which I didn't recognise had been flung over his body. It was as I lifted it to gaze upon his lifeless face that, for the first time, real, true panic assailed me.

The bullet had entered his back and made its way out through the left breast. As I sorrowfully lowered the strange cloth over him again, I noticed that my own body was shivering uncontrollably all over: I could almost hear my insides shaking against my bones! With my thoughts tossing about like balls in a fountain, I took a step back from the corpse—and, as I moved, I saw in the corner of my eye a piece of white material draped over the branches of the scrub. I realised that it was Miyazawa's "thousand-stitch belt", that he had washed only that morning and which was just getting dry: and with the realisation, again there came again that panic, that dread that I can't find words for and that racked me and set up the shivering right through my body. I could not bring myself to go back inside our shelter; I had to get away from the place and I set off wandering through the jungle again, my feet just taking me where they wished.

Almost at once, I was attacked by a terrible sense of quite unbearable loneliness. I reached our cave and decided to spend the night there. I could not get off my mind the

75

image of the face of the dead Miyazawa and I know I hardly slept a wink. I kept thinking: why hadn't they buried the corpse and fired the shelter? This was the way they always did it. I could not understand why they'd not acted according to their normal practice.

But as it turned out I was mistaken, for when I went back again to our shelter in the evening of the following day, I found a fresh heap of earth over Miyazawa's corpse. The shelter itself had been completely gutted.

Early the following morning, I took myself off to the hiding place of Minakawa and Umino.

"I can't possibly stay alive on my own...." I spoke from experience. And they readily agreed to take me in with them.

Thinking about it afterwards, I decided that the attack on our shelter had come from the Chamorro tribe all right; however, it was probably not a patrolling group but rather a single hunter after deer. I couldn't stop myself thinking about it, over and over again; if it *had* been a patrol, they'd have been sure to have had automatic rifles. But that bastard had picked off Miyazawa with a single bullet—for all the world as though he were taking a pot shot at a stag.

"But it was the smell of the fat cooking that did it," I kept reiterating to Minakawa. "Maybe it was the dog getting a scent of the fat that started it all."

"It looks as though there isn't much doubt that it was a hunter out on his own," Minakawa concluded. "And then he went back again today, this time with a patrol, to set fire to the shelter and to bury the corpse—the bastard, the rotten, stinking bastard."

"We heard the gun all right," said Umino. "But we didn't connect it with your shelter at all. We thought it was very likely a hunter banging off at a stag or something; you see, there was only that single shot."

8

The First Expedition for Salt Water

On the following day, we moved our hiding place further again to the south-west. The place we chose nestled in a fold halfway up the mountain, just over five hundred yards away, but it was badly off for food and we were very soon on the move again, this time far to the south, by the upper waters of the river Talofofo. It was during this move that I first learnt that Umino also possessed a gun. It was a Japanese army pistol, but he was extremely cagey about it, keeping his ammunition from our sight.

The place we had moved to was an upland terrace, about three miles across, and was due west of a village called Talofofo, after the river. If I remember correctly, the aboriginals used the name Finlan for this part of the forest.

Before the American landing, our Company had been stationed in this area for a period of two or three months, so it was a region where we had spent many busy days in the camp compound. Our move from the north was for two main reasons—first, that we understood the search for Japanese soldiers hiding up in this region had already been completed; and secondly, perhaps the more telling of the reasons, that since we were about to enter another rainy season, we wanted to be living somewhere where there was a plentiful supply of food.

A further reason for our choice lay in the fact that there was a good deal of rock here and that, dotted about in the hills, there was a fair number of caves which could be used as hiding places. However, in that the great majority of these caves were on the side of the mountains which faced towards the north, we decided to shun them and chose instead, as a site for our new hiding place, a patch of thick

77

scrub which even a master huntsman would have had difficulty in penetrating.

There were a good many undulations in these hills, which provided ideal places for concealment in the event of any emergency. As I remember it, it was in the May of 1947 that we made our move, our bodies completely laden with all our most precious possessions. Copra, coconuts, bananas and such-like grew luxuriantly in the dense forest, but the season was still a little early for the fruit to be properly ripe.

Our life together continued harmoniously enough. There were many days when the three of us went out as a party in search of food. However, it was from about this time that we all three began to suffer excessive fatigue: when climbing a mountain slope, for example, we felt a heaviness that defies description. And though there was nothing you could put your finger on as an actual ailment, day followed day when we just flaked out—even quite early in the morning—and could find no urge to stir ourselves for the rest of the day.

"Perhaps it's something to do with an enervation which comes from the insufficiency of salt in our bodies,"—the suggestion came from Umino. Umino was fond of describing himself as a "raw recruit", but back home as a civilian, he had been some sort of minor local official and there were times when his attitudes and his outlook showed him to be almost a race apart from us farmers.

We had been putting this lassitude down simply to a lack of nutritional value in our diet, but when we realised it was caused by an insufficiency of salt, we thought at once, of course, of the sea.

We calculated that it was between a mile and a mile-and-a-half from where we were. There were times when you could hear the sound of the waves after nightfall.

"Let's go and collect some sea water and boil copra leaves in it, shall we?" I suggested to the other two.

However, there was a major snag—for even here there

78

was still no way of reaching the coastline without crossing the road used by American service vehicles. From the hill-top, I watched the road, which ran along the coastline from north to south; jeeps, trucks and passenger vehicles passed regularly to and fro, all looking like toys from my distant vantage point. And between the road and me there was a stretch of open ground, not unlike pasture-land.

"It'll involve a fair amount of risk," said Minakawa, who, as I think I have said before, was always the one for caution.

"But don't you see, if we can't get some salt inside us, we're all as good as done for. And I, for one, don't want to die a lingering death that way." Umino spoke in a reproving tone.

With this, we made up our minds to come down off our hill as the sun was beginning to set. We idled away the rest of the day as we waited for the time to move.

As the sun sank, we made our way to the top of a slope from which we were able to look down on the plain below. On my back, I carried in my rucksack an empty tin which would take about four gallons, which we had picked up in the rubbish dump.

We waited on the edge of the plateau until the sun had vanished completely. Now and again, one could see vehicles with their lights on, returning towards the camp zone. And when we thought there were not likely to be any more pass-ing, we at long last set off down the slope and began crossing the meadow land. There wasn't a light to be seen anywhere. Bending almost double, we cut across the pasture and then, just before we got to the road, we stretched ourselves flat on the ground.

The road, magnificently paved, glimmered before our eyes, as white and gleaming as a river in moonlight. To the eye, it looked to be twenty yards or a bit more across.

"Let's get across one by one, shall we?" I whispered to Umino, turning on my side to face him.

"Who's going to go first?" I heard him whisper back.

"I'll go in front..." I replied.

79

I looked carefully up and down the road. Over on the other side, a thick grove of coconut palms painted what was clearly, even in the dark of the night, a South Seas silhouette against the starry sky.

"I'm off, then..." I muttered, and I scrambled across the road for all I was worth.

There was a dense tangle of scrub bordering the far side. I forced my way blindly into the heart of it, the sound of the sea killing all the disturbance and racket that I created. I turned round to look back from my hiding place in the undergrowth. There was not a sign of a headlight in either direction. As I switched my gaze to the other side of the road, I caught a glimpse of someone setting off to scamper across. It was Minakawa. And soon Umino had forced his way through the undergrowth to our side.

"This grove's as safe as you could hope for, don't you think?" said Umino, his words coming between desperate gulps for breath. But neither of us could find anything to say in reply to this, and presently we set off in the direction from which we could hear the waves, forcing our way through a dense forest of scrub overhung by the tall palms. The thicket ended after about fifty yards and the whole vista of the sea opened up before our eyes. For a while we stood and gazed at the dark water. It looked to be a mere fifteen or sixteen steps to the nearest point on the beach where the waves were lapping. I started to run towards the water. For the first five or six steps, I felt as though I was walking on sand, but then the surface became harder underfoot, and I guessed that the sand had given way to rock. We prospected a little to the south, searching for a convenient inlet among the boulders. As soon as we had found one, I judged the moment when the sea would recede between waves, waded in to fill the can with sea water, and scrambled hastily back to dry land.

We took turns at drinking the sea water. The moment it settled on my stomach, I had an immediate feeling that my energy and vigour were rapidly returning. This must have

For one thing, this was less cumbersome to walk with; it was far less bulky if ever we needed to move house again; and, into the bargain, it came to be regarded as a valuable necessity in case of illness—it made a perfect "water-pillow"!

We had picked up tyres and inner tubes at the rubbish dump, but we usually found them discarded by the side of the vehicular road. It would seem that American servicemen lived in such luxury that they never got round even to contemplating using again a tyre with the smallest puncture. Their general practice seemed to be to jettison them without the least sign of regret! Fortunately for us.

But we didn't just go barging down the hill to pick up regardless every tyre we happened to find thrown out by the roadside. We were not to know whether an abandoned tyre was in fact part of some trap set for us. Suppose they went back to pick up the punctured tyre, and realised it was not where they had left it—this would tell them that there were stragglers lying up somewhere in the neighbourhood. . . .

Under no circumstances did we wish our existence to become known; as a result, our greatest fear was to leave behind us even that one footprint which would lead to discovery. So, if ever we happened to find a tyre, we would either leave it exactly as it was for a few days or we would hide it somewhere a very short distance from the road. If nothing had happened to it after a few more days, then and then only would we carry it home to our hiding place. We had used these strict rules for all the tyres and inner tubes that had come into our possession. We used tyres to make sandals, and an inner tube, cut in two and with one end blocked up, made an excellent receptacle for storing water.

As far as drinking water was concerned, our rule was, as far as possible, to avoid river water and only use rainwater. This was because we found even the river water to contain a coral constituent. We knew that an impure sediment, which was white in colour, would be found on tins which we had used for storing river water, and that before very long this impurity would begin to cause corrosion.

We worked out a means of collecting rainwater. We cut an inner tube, placed it so that it was supported vertically by a tree trunk with one end pointing upwards, and fitted into this upper end a kind of funnel made of large leaves. When rain fell, the tube filled with water immediately. With a hole near the base of the tube and a wooden stopper fitted to this hole, we found ourselves rid of all the inconveniences of empty tins and cans and water-carrying, furnished as we were with something almost as good as piped water and taps.

"But rubber's not very good for you, is it? Couldn't it set up some sort of poison inside you?" asked Minakawa, always the cautious one. It was a nuisance, but he might be right: we took notice of his warnings and from then on used our rubber tanks only when we felt there to be some risk of an attack; when we felt no such danger, we used the more cumbrous and obvious tin cans.

9

Raw Lizard

We moved to a new hiding place and at the same time I hid my rifle in a spot about eighty yards from our shelter. The site I chose was a tiny cave, an absolute dream of a place, quite ideal for hiding my gun, a change of clothing and other such prized possessions.

That night I spoke to Umino, who was having a quiet lie-down.

"Umino, I think you'd do far better to hide your gun somewhere. After all, you know, it's a very valuable thing to have—something you'd never lay hands on again if you lost this one."

"But you always have yours around, don't you?"

"No, I don't. Not here, at least. No—if there was a flap,

and I had to cart a gun with me, it would slow up my move-ments no end, wouldn't it? And again—how often do you have need of a gun, except for shooting a cow? I think you'd be far better off to hide it somewhere, I really do. . . ."

"Oh well, that's where we disagree then, isn't it?" Umino's reply had more than a hint of anger. "I keep it with me as a precaution. If I hid it somewhere else and there was an emergency, I wouldn't be able to lay hands on it in time, now would I? I've no intention of letting some swine Guam native blow *my* brains out, you know."

"But, with it hidden here in the shelter, suppose there was an attack while we weren't here and your precious gun was carted off; what then? That's the end of you having a gun isn't it?"

"Dear God! You ought to know me well enough by now to be sure I wouldn't make such a balls-up of hiding it, surely!" Umino clearly wasn't planning to let his gun out of his hands.

The conversation ended on that note. And although Umino refused point blank to stop this practice of hiding his gun inside our shelter, our life together still proceeded smoothly and peacefully. Perhaps this was because I real-ised that one could never survive on one's own, and so, in spite of occasional flarings of temper, I strove my utmost to grin and bear it and keep my mouth tight closed.

The rainy season ended and, with the coming of the dry weather, we began to notice the activities of patrols once more.

One such day, we had walked in search of food following the course of the river Talofofo and then along the foot of the line of hills stretching to the west. We knew that there was a veritable banana treasure house on the other side of the marsh to our left, and we had come out specifically to gather bananas. Presently, when we had come down off the hill and were crossing the marshy zone, Minakawa ex-claimed: "Hey! Look—there—it's a shelter, surely..." and he pointed at the dense scrub to our left.

85

The entire area was reed-covered, with the exception of the part indicated by Minakawa's finger, which was dense forest with an unusual blackish tinge. Although there was no tenting or tarpaulin, there were clear traces of a shelter there. Making our tongue-click warning noise, we went cautiously up to it, and though there were no signs of anyone there, in front of the dead scrub there was a disused tin can. I picked it up, had a good sniff at it, and recognised the smell of cooked bananas.

"It looks as though they've only just moved," I said to Minakawa, putting the tin can under his nose.

"A patrol, I bet...." Umino, in spite of himself, looked anxiously round behind him. "Looks as if they've got natives in these parts, too. I think we'd better make our way back again. Judging by this smell, they must have been living here until yesterday or the day before. I suppose they felt it wasn't too safe and moved off somewhere."

We decided not to go any further, so we began to retrace our steps, with a weird feeling that we were being followed. I heard Umino grumbling and cursing away at himself for not bringing his precious gun with him, but neither Minakawa nor I broke the silence as we walked.

That day we moved our hiding place to the highest ground in the vicinity; the site we chose was on a pretty steep slope facing south. In that the area abounded in "rose potato" bushes, the spot was ideally suited for the months to come.

However, it was still a little too early in the season and the "rose potatoes" were not ripe enough for eating; so we spent several days nursing empty stomachs and resting or sleeping. It was this sort of situation, with none of us bothering to venture a word, and with precious little to do but sit tight and wait, that usually brought on a feeling of despair, a hopelessness edged with the dark shadow of death.

Of course, one knew well enough that the cause of the feeling of despair lay in the fact that we were unable to lay our hands on any subsidiary article of diet which was of nutritional value; and it made things no better when a succession of fruitless hunting expeditions meant that we hadn't caught even so much as a wood-mouse. "Should we try eating lizard, do you think?" I asked on one occasion—the idea prompted by the sight of one of these reptiles drinking water at a hill stream.

"He's far too fast for you—you'd never be able to kill him." This was Minakawa's not very hopeful response.

"It'd be fine if we made some wire netting and caught him with that." I was speaking my thoughts out loud.

In the state we were in at the time, our vitality completely sapped, the thought even of lizard flesh was quite enough to excite the fascination of the unknown. And once some new, positive objective had come into being, we were promptly urged to action. The making of the netting was allocated to me, as being the one with the best pair of hands among us. I finally contrived a piece of thin-mesh netting from some fine wire that we'd picked out of the rubbish dump. The plan was to beat the lizard to death with a pole when its legs had got caught in the mesh.

We knew that, in the dry season, the lizards used to seek out mountain streams, so we planned to entice them with a tin of water and then catch one in our net.

What with the continued lack of food, it took me all of two days to make the netting. But once this was done, our little plot couldn't have gone better. A large lizard—it must have been all of three feet long—came up at once to drink from our water-can; we looked at each other, trying hard to conceal our broad grins. We stood stock-still, like so many trees, while the lizard, without a care or caution in the world and tricked by our decoy water, began to drink. We chose our moment and had the net over him in a flash. The lizard's feet were caught in the mesh and while he writhed and wriggled to free himself, one of us, ready with a thick pole, beat him to death. Our little plan had been a perfect success, and, for the first time in all our lives, we were about to eat lizard meat broiled in salt! But we were in for the saddest of disappointments—lizard meat proved far too greasy and "raw" to be anywhere near suiting our tastes.

Umino was the first to put his chopsticks aside in disgust. "There's far more taste in a wood-mouse, don't you think?" he shuddered. He was quite right. We couldn't raise any enthusiasm for having another go at catching lizards!

We next turned our efforts towards hunting deer. But at that time—it was about 1948—we had not acquired either the intelligence or the patience that was needed to quarry a stag, and we packed this in with nothing more achieved than a distant sight of what we thought might have been a hind.

There was a long succession of days when we ate nothing apart from "bread preserve"—our name for breadfruit that we had treated in such a way that it would keep. First we heated the fruit, then we allowed it to dry out thoroughly; we gave it the name "dried bread" and kept it enclosed in the old shell-case. This "dried bread" was quite invaluable to us in our efforts to tide ourselves over the period between the availability of our main articles of diet, and, as a result, it was among the items which we always made it a rule to conceal in a nearby cave.

This shows what we were reduced to at lean times in the year—here we were treating as a luxury and as a vital essential food that wasn't fit even for pigs! We learned to bury "rose potatoes" in the ground to help us over the between-period which lasted from April to May: but these kept, at best, only for two or three weeks. However, we finally discovered that "rose potatoes", too, could be dried and that in this condition they could be preserved for a fairly long period; so this was, at long last, the end for us of what had always been the imminent risk of—in the literal sense of the words—starvation conditions.

10

The Dream of Escape From the Island

It was now six years since we had landed on Guam. One had only to allow one's thoughts to play ever so briefly round the fear that an attempt to land and retake the island might actually have been launched, and have come to grief, to be assailed by a despair so oppressive and unbearable that one was almost carried away by the urge to scream at the top of one's voice.

One such day, when it all seemed to be getting too much for me, and I was fretting away impatiently, I wondered if I might work some of it out of my system if I went to collect some sea water. So I waited for the sunset and set off, an old inner tube over my shoulder. Minakawa came with me.

We pushed our way silently through the jungle and came out on the mountain track that traces a diagonal half way up the hill. Then we turned in the direction of the sea, still moving as quietly as we could, taking care to kill the sound of our footsteps and keeping a close watch both in front of and behind us.

It was just over a mile to the shore from where we were. If we had carried on along the same track, we should have come out on to a paved road which goes through to Taro village, but it had become our usual practice to turn off from this track part way along it, and cut back into the jungle, emerging at the eastern tip of the range of hills.

By the time we had made our way to the hill from which we always dropped down to the shore, it was completely dark.

Sharing a mood, we both slumped down on a rock overgrown with scrub and gazed dreamily at the pitch-black sea. Now and again, we could see the headlights of a vehicle winking along the paved road which led from north to south between the pasture land and the shore. There were two hours to wait before we dared go down.

A huge tree above our heads blotted out one half of the sky; as I must have done many hundreds of times before, I mulled over why it was that I'd come to this sort of hell on earth. Oh, blast, I thought; if it hadn't been for this bloody war, right now I'd be back home in the village, nestling in the mountains. My mother and father and my kid sister and I would be round the hearth, talking and laughing away together after our supper.

Minakawa's low voice broke into my self-pitying dreams. "Itō—I can see a light from a ship!"

I sat up quietly. In the darkness where the sea and the sky merged, there were half a dozen or so lights which looked like fishing-beacons: they bobbed about in the sea as I watched. "They look like bonito-boats to me; what do you say?"

"Right first time! They're bonito-boats or I'm a Korean," Minakawa replied. With that we both of us fell silent, watching the boat beacons closely.

"They're boats from Taro, are they?" I wondered aloud at last.

"I suppose they could be."

"I wonder? Do you think the war might be over?"

There was no direct reply from Minakawa. "They must be pretty large fishing boats. I bet you could get to Japan in a boat as big as that. What would you say?" he asked absently.

I realised that I'd just been thinking exactly the same thing myself. Startled, I looked at Minakawa's profile. "If you had a boat that size, and if you sailed north along the Marianas, you could certainly get as far as Ogasawara," I said. "Then, if you went due north from Ogasawara, you should get to Japan, shouldn't you? If you could manage to strike a following wind, then you might well get right through, you know."

"I wonder how many days it'd take you?" Minakawa was

90

mulling over what I'd said. "Itō, can you manage an engine?"

"No, I haven't a clue."

"Neither have I, worse luck. I wonder if Umino would be any good?"

"I wouldn't know...." As I replied, for some reason or other, there flashed across my mind the vision of Umino's gaunt and disagreeable face.

But Minakawa was fast becoming carried away by his idea. "If none of us knew anything about an engine, then we'd have to make some tenting into a sail and manage it that way. If we used our judgement and timed it for the season when the early autumn wind blows, I dare say we could sail it in about a fortnight." Minakawa spoke decisively, as if he had no doubts about it. We gazed at each other with wide eyes.

So this talk of getting away from the island, which had started only as a piece of fanciful day-dreaming, had now, somehow or other, turned into a matter of close and weighty concern for all three of us. It was bound to have happened to us sooner or later, I suppose: the birth of an idle fancy of escaping from these circumstances, however reckless and crude the idea was, and however unrelated it might be to our true intentions; and now it was beyond our powers to suppress this fancy, burgeoning as it was with hope.

We started planning. We could rely on rainwater for drinking purposes while we were at sea. For food, we'd take on board a store of dried "rose potatoes" and breadfruit. Any bonito we happened to catch would come in as additional food. All such topics were gravely argued and decided. And in the matter of the timing of our escape, it was settled that the typhoon season, when winds were strong, was the most suitable.

Little by little, preparations went ahead. We contrived leisure moments to make fishing-hooks and put down a supply of "dried bread"; and in all these activities the three

91

of us worked together and pooled our energies in a way that had never happened before—to such a degree were we drawn together and linked by this single, joint objective.

We moved our hiding place from time to time, and still did not abandon our preparations, edging bit by bit towards our hopeful dream.

During intervals between foraging expeditions, or on dull and gloomy days when we were kept in by the rain, I busied myself carving seals on the stag's antler that I had picked up in the jungle. At such moments I became so absorbed that I even forgot the time. I had made myself a carving tool by tempering one of the thick bed springs that we had picked up in the American rubbish tip.

"By gosh, you're a clever one, aren't you?"—even Umino was showing an interest in life nowadays, which was quite out of character!

"Oh! That's on account of one of the customs back home in my village; even when you're quite young, they teach you how to use one of these knives." I went on working, and didn't lift my eyes as I replied.

I started off with a seal for myself, then went on to do one for Minakawa, and others for all manner of names, such as Tanaka, Akaike, and so on. Before I'd finished, I'd accumulated a store of several dozen.

"Whatever are you going to do with them? All you do nowadays is make seals...."

I laughed as I replied to Minakawa's question. "They'll do for presents when we get home. Surely everyone'll be very glad to be given one, especially when I say they're made from the antlers of a Guam stag!"

After this, seal-carving became my chief diversion for the whole period that we were on Guam. Some of the seals I stored away carefully along with my valuables in my secret cave; others I jettisoned and lost whenever we were nosed out and chased by aboriginals.

* * *

Two full years had now slipped by since we had conceived our plan of escape from the island. Preparations were all completed: all that remained to be done was to find a boat. We had a supply of "dried bread" and "dried potatoes" stored up carefully in the old American naval shell-case and in a collection of square tin cans. Our supply would easily keep body and soul together for the three of us for a good fortnight or so and these stores were hidden away safely in a cave as close to the shore as was practicable and yet secure.

The final episode in the story of our attempt to escape occurred in the September of that year—which was 1952.

The umpteenth typhoon was blowing with a violence fit to tear out by the roots every tree on the island. At this sort of time, all we could do was lie low, cowering in our shelter. We had no means of keeping off the rain. The best we could manage was to squat with our chins between our knees, under the protection of a piece of tarpaulin slung so low that even as we squatted, our heads nearly touched it; like stone statues, we would wait motionless and quiet for the storm to blow itself out.

This season always used to feel the coldest in the whole year. For while we were being subjected to, and trying our best to ride out, a savage battering from nature in the shape of a typhoon, and had our energies thus fully employed, we could make little showing against the additional assault of the cold. Though it probably was nowhere near so severe, it certainly felt something like the cold you get in November in Japan.

At times like this, I felt that, try how I might, I couldn't stop myself from boiling over in quite unrestrainable rages. Sometimes, the only way to calm the wrath was to shout and scream for all one was worth! And however loud the shouts and screams, the clatter of the storm winds swallowed them up, so that one could hardly hear them oneself—which meant it was safe to do it!

It was two days after the storm, as I remember, that

Minakawa and I, just the two of us, set off for the coastline with the idea of searching for a boat at long last. We had left Umino behind in our hiding place, for, from about this time, his health was beginning to fail and he was starting to show signs of growing weaker. He would cough violently from time to time and spit up enough phlegm to fill his whole palm. Because of this, we did not dare to leave him in the daylight, and it was sunset before we eventually set out from our shelter. Our first objective was the area of the estuary. We started from the part of the river valley which had once been the Headquarters of the Company to which I had been attached, and worked down from there towards the river mouth, keeping close to the bank all the way.

However, all that we could see when we came to the estuary were canoes; there was not the slightest sign of anything you could really call a boat. For two nights running, Minakawa and I combed every place that looked like a harbour or a landing place on the entire eastern seaboard of the island; but our efforts, after all, led us absolutely nowhere: we'd still to set eyes on a single real boat.

What we did manage to see, merely rubbed in our plight worse than ever: it was the American service barracks, ablaze with light. From a garden inside the compound, the notes of a jazz tune came wafting to us on the breeze. The figures of the soldiers and their women dancing away merrily looked to us, from our distant viewpoint, like a group of puppets. But puppets very much to be envied!

We could neither of us manage a single word. The sense of utter defeat, too overwhelming to allow of any description, numbed our entire bodies and all our senses. After a while, we dropped down a steep slope and began trudging despondently, our feet dragging listlessly, along the paved cross-country road which led from the east right across to the west coastline. Just as we were about to cut off on to a mountain track through the jungle, after we'd crossed a flat stretch of pretty grassland to which we'd given the nickname "the drill-ground", we heard at our backs a dog barking furiously. We dived off the road at full tilt, and fled into the dense scrub. And, fortunately, there was no sign that the dog wanted to give chase....

We realised, of course, that we could have found a boat if we had come down on to the *western* coastline of the island. But we also realised that to do this, to get down to the shore on that populous side of the island, was tantamount to walking to the slaughterhouse on our own two feet.

So our plan to escape from Guam remained a dream; and like all dreams, it vanished eventually into thin air....

11

A Trap?

Now that our hope of escape was blighted, we became curiously crotchety and ill-tempered with each other. It was hard to stop yourself feeling that everything had lost all purpose. The war and its outcome—whether we won or lost—no longer seemed to be of any concern to any of us.

Very soon after this, we again moved our hiding place up to the higher ground. We did this because we knew from past experience that a change of site and surroundings was often quite effective in inducing a change of mood.

One day not long afterwards, along with Minakawa and Umino, I had set off early in the morning on a food and foraging expedition. We had crossed a couple of valleys, climbed up a slope, traversed a narrow path through the dense scrub-land, and were just coming out on to the road that runs along the foot of the hills when my eye suddenly rested on something quite unusual: it looked to me to be some sort of parcel. And it appeared to have been dropped by someone on the weeds that grew at the side of the road.

"Whatever could it be?" I muttered to myself, and, not stopping to think, I stooped to pick it up. The wrapping was of vinyl—something of which I did not know the existence at the time, and which helped to give the parcel a part of its fascination for me.

"Itō!—It's damned silly to pick up that sort of thing," said Minakawa, trying to snatch it out of my hands. "It's quite on the cards that it's been put there by some of the aboriginals as a trap for us. It'd be best, I think, to leave it just where it is."

But I'd got the urge—and no one was going to stand in my way—to take that parcel home. The two of them did all they could to stop me, but I waved aside all their objections and refused to put it down again. During the whole of the time we were walking back to our shelter, they kept on making attack after attack on my lack of judgement and discrimination; but, undaunted (and this was unusual for me in that I normally respected their opinion), I arrived home still carrying the parcel.

I was astonished to find that it contained a couple of dozen Japanese pencils made by Mitsubishi, all beautifully sharpened and ready for use.

From the time that we had come to Guam until about 1946, I had kept a simple record of what I remembered best in an issue service diary. But this diary had been lost when our shelter was attacked and burnt down. Then, in about 1949, I had picked up a diary and a pencil in the American rubbish tip, and had been using this second volume to record my recollections of the main events from 1949 onwards. I still possessed this second diary at the time the parcel was found. But the pencils would certainly come in useful.

First, I smelled them—it was good, that smell of Japanese wood again—then I ran my fingers through a thick writing pad; and, finally, I opened an envelope which I had also found in the parcel on which was printed the heading "Army, Navy; Japanese Government, Demobilisation Section."

Inside the envelope was a long duplicated letter. I let my

96

eye run through the text, almost voraciously. I cannot remember the entire contents or the precise wording, but the
gist of it was something like this:

To All Who May Read This Communication

*We thank you for the way in which you have lived
your lives on behalf of Japan, and we rejoice that you
have survived.*

*We are fully aware how trying and painful circum-
stances must have been for you, and we realise that you
have suffered, over a period of eight and more long years,
continued trials and hardships.*

*But, every moment now, the dawn comes nearer—the
dawn that will mark the close of this long and dismal
existence; now, brave hope and great gladness await each
one of you. As an example, let us quote you the experience of seven men, soldiers or attached civilians, who
were in similar circumstances to the rest of you in the
northern part of Guam and who, the year before last
(1951), made overtures to the Americans and received
hospitable and generous treatment at their hands; they
now live pleasant and comfortable lives with their loved
ones back in the homeland.*

*If you find that you cannot bring yourselves to believe
these facts, we would ask you to make use of the paper
enclosed in this same envelope and to write down your
ideas and impressions for your family. We will make it
our business to ensure these are communicated to your
family and we undertake that their reply, when received
by us, will be deposited in the same place where you discovered this parcel and this communication.*

At this point, I forget certain words and sentences, but
the communication went on to mention the grief in the
hearts of the families in Japan who had had no news of their
sons and who had presumed that they had been killed in

97

action. And there was a further message which began bravely, I remember:

All of you who were presented with our glorious national flag, the emblem of the rising sun ...

And there were two signatures, one of them Nagashima and the other a name which began with Ita ... something-or-other. There followed a series of headings, detailing:

The progress of events affecting Japan since the time when all of you who read this document departed from Japan.

These were in question and answer form; and among the items were the following:

Q. *What is the outcome of the Great East Asia War?*

A. *The war was brought to an end as a result of Japan's suing for an armistice in August, 1945.*

Q. *Attendant on the termination of hostilities, what has happened in the case of Japanese Army and Naval forces?*

A. *Under the provisions set out by the American Forces, the Japanese Army and Navy have been completely demilitarised and personnel have been returned to their homes and families and have been directed to engage in productive occupations and activities. A statement known by the name of The Potsdam Declaration has the following clauses relevant to your own situation ...*

I will not go in to further details.

To this day, I remember how I read this letter over and over again. "So, maybe Japan *was* defeated, after all," I reflected; my thoughts were still not collected and the full impact of the letter had yet to hit me. As I thought round

"The naval bombardment started. It was the nearest approach to Hell I shall ever experience." In July 1944 American troops returned to Guam with overwhelming forces. "From our commanding heights we watched this vast flotilla of craft pushing towards the shore like a huge flock of water spiders."

ABOVE: Men and supplies pour on to the shell-torn coast, after the terrific bombardment had smashed Japanese shore positions, and prepare for the ferocious battle inland.   BELOW: Japanese pillboxes are no match for the power of the American field-guns.

ABOVE: "The Headquarters message blandly told us to resist stubbornly and work for the piecemeal destruction of the enemy." U.S. Marines move into Rota Peninsular. BELOW: Marines attack Japanese positions across a rice field. The man on the right has just thrown his grenade.

"So it was to be guerilla fighting. As far as the Americans were concerned, we were just a mopping-up operation no doubt. But for us, it was survival or extinction." Explosive charges burst inside a Japanese dugout on Rota Peninsular.

"For us soldiers of Japan, the only thing left, to our way of thinking, was to deck out our last moments as nobly and bravely as we could." Japanese dead sprawled over Rota Peninsular after the attack by the 77th Army Division.

ABOVE: "Like so many rabbits hounded by a dog, the three of us lurked in our respective shelters." This is the sort of hideout which, for sixteen years, was home.

LEFT: "We scoured the army dump. We used empty tins and cans to make pans. We made sewing needles out of bedsprings. We made water carriers out of discarded truck tubes." Scraps of equipment which kept the stragglers alive in the jungle.

United Press International

"The grinning young American handed me a shirt and some long trousers. I was handed a pair of pyjamas. I felt they were going to a lot of trouble if we were merely going to be shot." Itō (*left*) and Minakawa at the Guam Naval Hospital, 1960.

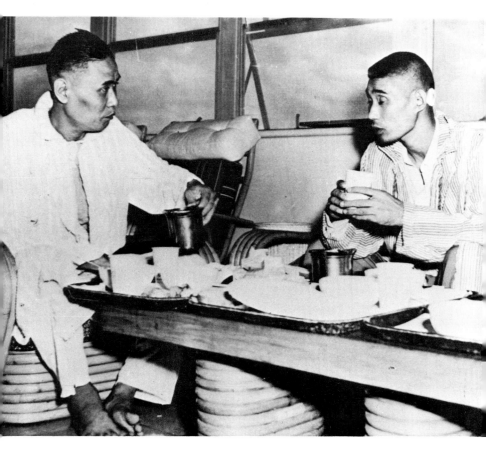

"God, that food tasted marvellous. There was a pile of bread whiter than I'd ever imagined bread could be. I was still sure it was part of a plot." Itō (*left*) and Minakawa at the Guam Naval Hospital.

"The press conference at Tachikawa Air Base was an exact replica of the one in Guam. We had lived so long in the dim light of the jungle that the glare of the lamps dazzled us. A hundred newspaper-men were pushing their way into the room."

"The photographers seemed fascinated by my topknot. It had not been cut for sixteen years."

Itō in front of his home.

"I wished to God they'd all leave me alone. I wanted, all on my own, to look at every single corner of our house."

"This morning at dawn I was back in the churchyard, standing in front of my own tombstone erected by my father."

"You're home; this is your home, I kept saying to myself as I shut my eyes. This isn't the jungle any more; there's no need to listen for any and every noise."

this new situation, however, I remembered something that had happened, I think it was, in 1946: at any rate it was while I was still living in the same shelter as Miyazawa and we had read a leaflet, the sense of whose contents was pretty well identical, although the wording might well have been different from that of this present communication.

On the previous occasion (in 1946, that is) a light plane had circled over us any number of times, dropping these leaflets. One of these had fluttered down to rest on a branch in front of our shelter. I remember going to pick it up, casually and with no particular interest. "Oh! I say! Look —it's printed in Japanese!" I remember shouting in my surprise.

There were two photographs on this leaflet—one of them showing a meeting between MacArthur and our Emperor, the other a meeting on board the battleship *Missouri* between MacArthur and Shigemitsu and Umezu. Underneath these photographs was a message which read:

The war is over. The Japanese Army has surrendered unconditionally and a meeting has taken place between The Supreme Commander, MacArthur, and the Emperor of Japan. This is no deception and no trap and Japanese military personnel should assemble without anxiety or concern at the Reception Centre at Agana, on the northern coast of Guam, where arrangements will be made to facilitate their early return to Japan.

At the time, we could only think that it was all an enemy trap. "War over indeed!" Miyazawa had snorted. "Japanese army surrendered! What kind of mugs do they take us for if they imagine we're going to fall for a load of tripe like that?" And we'd thrown the thing away.

But, on this occasion, it somehow felt just that bit different. "Supposing it *were* genuine..."—I could feel the idea gradually gaining hold of me. But neither Minakawa nor Umino would have anything to do with it.

99

"It's an enemy trap this time, too! What simple-minded fools we'd look if we were swindled into putting any faith in it!" They were clearly rejecting it flatly, and were not ready to give my interpretation the benefit of any doubt whatever.

"But, can't you see, you shouldn't overlook the possibility that it *might* just be above-board," I plugged on, with the idea of trying to argue them down. "Before you just reject it as flatly as you both have done, don't you think it'd be best to make *some* attempt, at any rate, to establish whether it's true or false?"

Then I had what struck me as a very bright idea. Supposing we did write a letter, but signed a false name, we should not be giving ourselves away at all! And then I suddenly hit on a name—Aihara, the friend who was killed in action on the day before the American landing.

I, too, had that nagging fear, you see, that if I signed anything in my own name, I would be revealing my existence! "Suppose we borrowed the name of one of the chaps we know bought it, and used that on a letter—we shouldn't be giving *ourselves* away at all, should we? Come on—what do you say to us signing Aihara's name?—And if we do get a reply, we'll know then that what this letter says is the truth. Let's try it, anyway—I can't see we've anything to lose."

I decided to ignore their objections and, grasping a brand-new pencil, I began to write my letter on the virgin pad of paper.

"It won't do you any good. I'd pack the whole blasted thing in, if I were you." I'd never seen Minakawa worked up like this before. But I paid no attention, and just let him shout as I began writing:

There's no need to worry about me, because I am alive and well in the jungle here. If this letter reaches you safely, please send me a letter from Tamako, in her own handwriting, and a photograph of all the rest of the

100

family. For the moment, remember I'm alive and safe and...

I knew all about Aihara having a younger sister called Tamako and it was partly because of this that I had decided that the Aihara family was perfect for my plan.

"Itō, do you really mean to go ahead and post it?" Minakawa shoved his face right under my nose as he spoke; he was glaring angrily at me and looking absolute daggers.

"Yes. To see whether it's all above-board or not; I'm going to leave it where we picked up the parcel." I started to put the letter inside the envelope. This was more than Umino could bear and he too began bawling at me, with the usual ghastly, grating tone in his voice.

"Itō! If you're not going to pay any attention to what we two say, then all there is left is for you to get the hell out of here and leave us to it. If you're going through with this crackpot scheme, I for one simply don't want you with us any more."

"He's right, you know, Itō. I don't think you're doing the right thing at all—even using a false name like this. If you are determined to go through with it and nothing's going to stop you from posting the letter, then the only thing is for us to part company here and now. I still think it's an enemy trap. And once you've fallen into the trap, just think of what it could lead to.... No! If *you* aren't going to get out, then *we* will. Once you post that letter, then you've only yourself to thank for the consequences." Minakawa spoke unusually forcefully for him.

In the end, all I could do was abandon my plan. I hadn't the guts to go against the wishes of the two of them together, and I kept warning myself that I just couldn't survive on my own.

So I decided to fall in with the decision of the majority and resigned myself to tearing up the letter. As I shredded the paper, I fell to thinking about Aihara. Supposing it were not a trap, supposing it had all worked and I *had* managed to get back home to Japan—supposing all this; however could I have explained it away to the dead Aihara's relatives? And when they heard what I had to say, would they even accept my story as the truth? I tried to picture Aihara's young sister, Tamako, weeping; would I ever be able to bring myself to face her again after what I would have done to her? And once my imagination had taken me this far, I gradually began to lose faith myself in the whole blessed thing.

"Ah, well..." I thought, "...it was good while it lasted." And, without saying a word, I slipped quietly out of our shelter and walked off silently into the jungle.

12

One of Us Departs

The dry season came round once more and, as usual, we moved our hiding place to the higher ground. However, the ties linking the three of us in outlook seemed to have slackened and it was quite impossible to run away any more from the impression that somehow we were all going against each other.

This feeling first began to take concrete shape in May and June the following year. For jungle bashers, as I've remarked before, this transition period is by far the most trying and distressing time of the whole year, when food is at its most scarce.

The origin of the affair was the question of labour (the most important part of which was to search for food) and the unequal apportioning of such food as we had managed to find.

"Itō—d'you realise you nearly always eat more than your proper share? It's unfair. From now on, I say we should divide our food strictly into three equal portions. Otherwise, there'll be a real bust-up." This, of course, was Umino, shouting at the top of his voice.

At this time, there were often days when we'd absolutely no reward for an entire day's tramping in search of food. We had consumed all we'd managed to put down and, after a whole day spent in searching, all that we'd managed to lay hands on to stave off starvation was grass roots and the new buds of a plant whose name we did not know. This, of course, negligible though it was, was the product of the labours of all three of us; but—and I have to say this, I'm afraid—I was always the one who managed to collect the most. Without any fear of contradiction, you could call me the hardest working and Umino the biggest drone of the three of us. The amount he managed to collect (all through the year, not only at this difficult transition period) was in fact less than the share he managed to eat! Even so, if ever Minakawa or I happened to eat more than we should, there was inevitably hell to pay from him. But, when all was said and done, I was easily the biggest eater of the three of us. I fully realised this and always did my very best, on account of this, to collect a greater amount than the other two.

"I should have thought it only fair that anyone who'd collected a lot of food should be allowed to eat a lot," I rejoined, my empty stomach making me irritable. "As for you, why should you think you can scoff the lot when you've only collected a piddling little amount? If you want to have a real good stuff, I suggest you start to do a bit more work."

It was evident that my hunger was driving me into the sort of state where my feelings would run away with me pretty easily. And there was more to it than this: by now I'd got quite a thing about Umino—for his always, from way, way back, picking on me and finding fault with me. For example, when I was starting a fire, he'd say, "Oh! Damn you! You make too much smoke, you do! If you made fires till kingdom come, you'd *always* make a mess of it. If we're spotted by a patrol, what the hell do we do then?"

His attitude reminded me of the way an old sweat corporal treats a raw recruit. Can you blame me if I couldn't manage to restrain my antipathy to him? If we were going to fling our rank around, anyway, then I suppose I would have taken precedence over Umino, who was a mere reserve. In the early days, I used to hold my tongue in face of his rantings, since I was very conscious of the fact that the request to be taken in with them had come from my side in the first place. But later on, I started to lose my temper and whenever he began to pile in to me, I stood my ground and gave him like for like.

"You put up a pretty fair smokescreen yourself," I snarled. "On the rare occasions when you condescend to make a fire. It seems to me you can never see any good in anything anyone else does."

That did it! "You, you bastard!" Umino shouted, thoroughly aroused now. "We let you come in with us out of the kindness of our hearts, and this is how you repay us! As you're only here on sufferance, anyway, I should have thought you owed it to us to work hardest to show your gratitude."

"Rubbish! How can you let someone slave his guts out and then never give him a reward? Anyway, I figure I've earned my place here by now—which is more than I can say for some people.... What's so strange about the one who works hardest eating the most, eh? And who works the hardest? Me...! If you want to eat as much as me, you'd just better take a look at yourself and begin to work a little harder, you miserable shirker!" I thought it would do no harm to ventilate my long-cherished ill-will against this boorish idiot, and so I let my temper spill over for once. But his reaction was more than I had bargained for.

"You stinking, rotten, stupid bastard," he raved hysterically. "How dare you—a dead-beat we picked out of the jungle—how dare you speak to me like that! Are you trying to tell me you aren't going to take any notice of what I say?"

He was blustering at me as though I was a professional no-good who could be cowed into submission if only he shouted loud enough!

"I know what it is," he went on, his face scarlet with rage; "you're doing this deliberately, aren't you, so that you can bitch up our life together? That's your little game, you illiterate peasant, isn't it? Well, let me tell you, when it comes to hard work, my grandfather was boss of a gang of navvies..."

I let him rage on. Had Minakawa been there, Umino's diversion into his family background—which always intruded into our quarrels—would have been his cue to sail in and make the peace between us. But he wasn't there: he had gone up to his own secret cave a few minutes before. Accordingly, my temper carried the wrangle a stage further.

"Our life together!" I shrieked. "What the hell do *you* know about communal life or working together? You haven't the vaguest inkling what work means; you're nothing but a good-for-nothing, lazy, shiftless shirker, living off Minakawa and me! And what gave you the idea you could lord it all over the place and order *me* around, I don't know...."

He glared at me, momentarily speechless. Now I had my teeth in, I was damned if I would let go either! "Who ever heard of a communal life as unequal as you want it?" I continued. "If you're going to create this fuss just because I happened to eat a bit more, then that settles it: we'll each work independently for our *own* food. From now on I'm blasted well eating with my own mouth every single scrap of food I collect and you'd better resign yourself to filling your stinking belly with your own dirty hands.... Just see how hungry you'll be when it's your own work that has to feed you—for there'll be no more cashing in on ours after this, I can promise you!"

105

"I knew it! I've always bloody well known it!" Umino burst out at last. "You filthy sod! You dirty little squealer, you! You're nothing more than an ignorant peasant bastard, you sod. . . ."

Almost weeping with rage, he stumbled away to his shelter. (Although we lived our lives communally so far as food went, we each had our separate shelters to live in at this time. There were a number of reasons for this: first, a shelter large enough to accommodate the three of us together was too large for our peace of mind; secondly, as long as we lived together, there was bound to be more gossip and chit-chat throughout the day—and the more we used our voices, the greater was the risk of discovery. The shelters were near enough for us to attract each other's attention with a tongue-click, our agreed danger signal. Another decision we had taken in consequence of this—which had an indirect bearing on my quarrel with Umino—was that the various tools and utensils we had gathered together to sustain life should remain the personal property of the individual, Lending and borrowing were strictly tabu. This was because, if one lost or mislaid such an article, the worry and labour involved in replacing it was so enormous that it was bound to bring the seeds of a dispute.)

Thinking this particular argument was now finished, I turned towards my shelter, still shaking inwardly with fury. Before I ducked to go in, however, something made me glance over my shoulder. Umino had come out again and was standing just behind me.

"I'm going to kill you, you bastard!" he seethed, raising the gun in his hands and aiming it at my chest. I heard a distinct click as he thumbed the safety-catch off.

I whirled, pushing up the barrel with one hand as I lunged out at him with the other. I still had enough strength to knock him flat, I was surprised to find. He went over backwards and careened into the scrub. A moment later he was up, his face a ghastly white and twitching with rage, as he flung away the gun and came at me with his bare hands. Umino was a gaunt man, not very solidly built, as I've said, and I was able to fell him again before he could touch me. This time, I gave him no respite, however, and leaped on him while he was still struggling to get up from the scrub.

The two of us were rolling in the undergrowth, kicking, biting and gouging in a life-and-death struggle, when Minakawa returned and managed to tear us apart. As he spoke the words of good sense and reason, we stood panting heavily, one on either side of him, glaring at each other. Later, when my temper had cooled, I felt ashamed of allowing my feelings to get the better of me like that and apologised for giving in to a momentary fit of passion with as much sincerity as I could muster. But Umino was totally unwilling to consider a reconciliation. He crept up to my shelter after dark with a lance he had made by fixing a sharp, pointed piece of metal to the end of a pole, then, looking as if he fully intended to cut off my head as I slept, he stole quietly and stealthily towards me, this lance at the ready.

As soon as I sensed him coming for me, I deliberately let him know that I wasn't asleep by giving a slight cough. At this Umino appeared to abandon his attempt and, with the tip of his lance flashing as it caught the moonlight, he slunk back dejectedly to his own shelter, silent as a cat.

Umino repeated this performance night after night. But my nerves had become so attuned and I was now so sensitive that I would waken even at the slightest rustle of a leaf; so I would catch the sound of Umino's footfalls, however much he strove to kill any sound, and I was always able to send him slinking off by using the same slight cough. On the other hand, if I'd been sound asleep, no doubt I'd have ended up cold with his lance through my chest!

I think it's quite on the cards that all Umino wanted to do was to intimidate me; he was trying to drive me out of the group by a war of nerves. This would explain the incident when we had our fight—I think he pointed his gun at me only to frighten me: and though he knew from the very first that the gun wasn't loaded, he still slipped the safety catch.

However, I was quite unable to bring myself to see it this way at the time. I used to sleep soundly, quite oblivious of the danger he posed. For I feared precious little from him and showed by this, no doubt, that my instinct had helped me see through him as being incapable of killing a man.

I told Minakawa what I felt.

"Yes, you're right. Umino could never kill anyone. All he can do is make himself so unpleasant you'd want to puke!" He laughed as he said this.

"I think so, too; and that's why I've never taken him on since that first time."

"Yes, you're doing the best thing possible, really. If you can't somehow meet each other half-way, then you'll neither of you come out of it alive, you see..."

It was not long after this that Umino announced, "I'm going to live on my own." He left our company and took himself off somewhere. For practically a year I never once set eyes on him, although, during that period, we ourselves must have moved our shelter at least a dozen times.

"I think he's probably taken himself miles away—perhaps way up north," I suggested once when we were discussing Umino and how frail he always looked.

"Could be. Personally, I've always thought he was a natural for T.B...."

Minakawa's suspicion tallied exactly with what I myself had often thought.

13

Reunion and Death

Once Umino had left our group and disappeared, Minakawa and I came to an agreement which would allow us each even further freedom and scope for individual action. We considered that this gave us the best, if not the only, hope of survival.

We agreed, for example, that, in the case of staple foods, each of us should eat only what he himself had managed to collect or find. Only in the case of subsidiary articles of diet did we share equally what the two of us had collected. We decided to continue living in separate shelters, keeping such a distance between us as would allow each to give the other warning of any danger. In addition, we agreed to continue not to lend or borrow tools or utensils. The outcome of this agreement was the creation of an even greater friendship between us.

We used to go out together on food foraging expeditions. And if, for instance, Minakawa climbed a tree to knock down breadfruit, I stayed underneath the tree all the time he was up it, not idly waiting for him but keeping a lookout. And similarly, while I was up a coconut palm, Minakawa would keep watch down below.

In the matter of subsidiary items of diet, supposing we did manage to come by an ox, we would divide it equally into two, deciding by lot who should take the parts he liked the most. And if all we had laid hands on was a miserable frog, this, too, we would split equally.

It was from about this time that we began to hunt deer. We'd heard it said that venison was extremely tasty, so we took it into our heads at least to give it a try. However, we knew well enough it was no easy task to quarry a stag, even if you were in a position to use a gun. We wondered on one occasion whether we might lay snares, in the hope of taking one of them alive. However, Minakawa had his usual cautious warning:

"No; I think the snare's risky. If we could be sure we could kill him the minute he fell into the trap, it might work. But supposing he were snared and started belling; he might well be discovered by a patrol! And the next thing would be that we'd be found out. We'd be setting a snare to catch ourselves instead, wouldn't we?"

At this point, we decided that the first thing to do if you want to take an animal alive is to turn yourself into an animal and learn its tricks. You must move with it, from jungle to crag, from crag back to jungle, and study all its habits.

But we did know one important thing already—that no stag will stool while it is on the move; so we could count on it stopping and standing still at such times. We could watch for this sort of chance and be in a position to grab it when it occurred; then we could go for him by the horns, and he'd be ours, we thought.

So we began from learning the tracks used by the deer. Then, one by one, we studied all its other habits—when it stooled, what sort of things it was likely to do just before it stooled, and so on. And it was not long before, from various postures and attitudes and other such indications which preceded the action itself, we were able to predict with a fair degree of accuracy just when it *was* going to stool. Now we were as proficient as this, all we had to do was wait patiently for a stag to start performing within range—three or four yards away from us, that is.

And we did once take a stag by these methods. But, to our great disappointment, venison—or the flesh from this particular animal—did not anywhere live up to its reputation and we concluded that stag-hunting was a waste of time and energy. So, after this one success, we gave it up.

* * *

By now it was almost a full year since Umino had parted

company with us. Following what had now become our regular practice, we moved our hiding place to the upper reaches of the Talofofo in preparation for the rainy season. The structure and siting of our hiding place on this occasion was slightly different from what it had been in previous years; we kept to our system of building separate shelters, but they now each led back into a small cave. In that it was just over four yards from my shelter to Minakawa's, we had no difficulty in passing signals between us.

I think it was five or six days after we'd moved there. I was squatting in front of Minakawa's shelter and arguing with him, in an undertone, about Buddhism. Minakawa, was, in fact, quite a staunch Buddhist.

Then, quite out of the blue, Umino appeared! He didn't make the slightest effort to talk to us, but started straight in to string a sheet of tenting in front of a cave about four yards away from Minakawa's shelter. He clearly intended to make this into his hiding place; it was less than ten yards from mine.

Umino had changed completely: you could hardly recognise in this gaunt and wasted figure the man who had left us twelve months before. He seemed to have weakened to an alarming degree. "He's living proof, after all, that it doesn't do to try to manage on your own," I muttered to myself. I didn't say anything, but I watched and listened to the rustling noises as Umino built his shelter.

"He looks pretty far gone," said Minakawa, turning his face in my direction. I didn't reply, merely nodding silently.

"It looks as if he's intending to move in with us, all right. I think it'd be best, don't you, to put him wise right now about the way we do things, we two, nowadays?"

I couldn't have agreed with Minakawa more, so together we went across to Umino's cave. He had by now finished stringing the tarpaulin in front of the cave mouth and he was lying flaked out inside.

When he realised we were there, Umino sat bolt upright,

staring up at us with a strange air of caution in his eyes. But he said nothing about us taking pity on him and having him in with us again. Minakawa and I squatted down in front of him and started in explaining all about how we managed things nowadays. Without so much as a nod even, Umino heard us out in silence. "You do see, don't you, we've agreed to organise it this way, because this is by far the most harmonious and peaceful way to carry on?" Minakawa repeated, trying to get things across to Umino and make sure he was paying some attention to what we were saying. At this Umino nodded meekly.

"You're feeling ill, aren't you, Umino?" I asked, trying to get a good look at him. I made my voice as sympathetic as I could.

"I'm pretty fagged out, that's all; but it's nothing that won't improve with three or four days' rest and sleep," the sick man replied shortly. And suddenly he broke into a fit of terrible coughing.

"Do you think you've picked up a cold somewhere?" asked Minakawa.

"Looks a bit like it, doesn't it?" Umino raised his hollow, sunken eyes up to us, and managed to twist his cheeks into the ghost of a smile.

Like so many rabbits hounded by a dog, the three of us lurked in our respective shelters. Umino, quite true to form, hardly ever opened his mouth to speak to us, though somehow he seemed to get enough food to keep himself going.

Even after he had rejoined us, we still kept to the rules we had made for ourselves and went shares only on subsidiary foods, which we divided equally between the three of us, first choice being settled by drawing lots. However, day followed day when we caught nothing and we were forced back on a daily ration of beef pickled in salt, which we boiled in water. And even this, which we'd meant to keep for a real emergency, would not last us very much longer at the rate we were going.

Minakawa and I trudged through the rain every day, combing the jungle for an ox. These were not the genuinely wild variety, but were pasture oxen which had taken to the jungle during the fighting and were now to be found roaming the mountains in a semi-savage state.

I still had the old repeater rifle which I had taken from the hand of the dead Australian. Since I had cut the barrel down and made it much less cumbersome to carry, I had found myself somehow becoming quite fond of it. I had shot my first ox with it early in September of the previous year.

Once, when we were out after oxen with my gun, Minakawa with his usual caution said: "If, by some mischance, the gun-shot happened to be heard by someone, it could have pretty grim consequences for us." So we made ourselves yet one more rule: never to fire a gun except when it was raining.

We calculated that the noise of the report would be stifled by the sound of heavy rain and we seem not to have been far out in our ideas, for even the oxen appeared to have their instincts dulled by the noise of the tropical downpours. They would seek refuge under the lee of a hill to avoid the worst of the winds and the rain, and we found that we could get quite near them—walking perfectly normally and not even bothering to kill the sound of our steps—and still not disturb them. With the wind swaying the tree branches, and the huge raindrops spattering down on the leaves of the jungle scrub, it was by no means difficult to get in a shot from quite a close range, long before the animal scented us.

I think I'm right in claiming that, with these methods, we bagged in all six oxen and one pig. These figures are based on the fact that, when we were finally taken by the Americans, we were told that there was only one bullet left in my gun. So I had fired seven shots; and in that I don't ever remember that I wasted a shot, this is the basis of my count—seven shots, seven hits!

I had never once kept my gun by me in my hiding place. In the early days, I used to keep it in a separate cave wrapped in a piece of cloth; later on, I used to hide it in a round metal cylinder which I had picked up in the rubbish tip. I cut this cylinder so that it was slightly longer than the gun itself, blocked up one end, buried it in the ground at an angle of thirty degrees so that the upper end protruded very slightly, and hid the rifle in it—concealing the visible end with dried leaves and stones. This allowed the free passage of air through the gun and meant that it was less likely to suffer from damp.

I moved the hiding place of the gun each time we moved our shelter, and never revealed where it was to a soul.

But to return to my story: Minakawa and I didn't have the good fortune to meet up with an ox that day either, so we had to be satisfied with carrying back a very modest haul of breadfruit.

When we got back, we poked our heads into Umino's shelter; as usual, he was lying flaked out, a glum and sour expression on his face. "What? You didn't go to work today either?" asked Minakawa.

"I went all right. But I didn't lay hands on a thing." Umino spat out the words.

We each gave him a breadfruit from our own haul, and he took them without so much as a thank-you. But by now we were too well used to Umino and his ways to find that this sort of thing jarred at all.

When we had first moved to this new home, there had been occasions when Umino had gone out with us on foraging expeditions; but he didn't seem capable of climbing high trees and so his haul was nearly always meagre in comparison with ours. Even so, he never asked us at first to share with him what we'd managed to get—because his pride just would not let him, presumably.

But his empty stomach wasn't to be fobbed off that easily; almost every day, he would eye the pile we'd brought in and then he'd invariably say, with a fair larding of sarcasm,

"You collected a hell of a lot, all right. Do you mean to say you feel like eating the whole damn lot?"

So we really could do precious little other than give him a part of what we had managed to gather.

However, this did not last for very long, for, quite soon, there were more and more occasions when Umino would not stir out of his shelter. He would lie flat on his back the whole day long and it became the routine—whether he used his sarcasm on us or not—for us each to share out with him a little of what we had ourselves collected. He would give in to his empty stomach, and begin to eat greedily; but after the first few mouthfuls, Umino would be overcome by a violent agitation, cough up an alarming amount of phlegm and then pant for breath.

On this particular day, too, Umino had only had a mouthful before the agitation began again. As we stroked his back for him, Minakawa and I involuntarily looked at each other.

"It'd be better, maybe, if you lay on your side, I'd think." As I spoke I pressed on his back and tried to ease him over.

"No, I can't. You see there's this terrible stiff feeling in my shoulders. Round here—can you feel it?—it seems pretty swollen to me...."

Even so, Umino didn't ask us to massage him; but although we were not asked, we took turns at squatting on our knees behind him and massaging the shoulders.

After a while, we tried him on something to eat again, but hardly had the first mouthful gone down before his body became terribly agitated and he began to writhe. He coughed up another mouthful of phlegm and this seemed to quieten him for a time; then he managed to get down another mouthful but, before long, the agitation and the restlessness had started up again.

Things went on like this for two or three days, and then, one evening, as we were taking turns to massage his shoulders, Umino suddenly blurted out, "My shoulder's so stiff I can't stand it any longer. You can massage as much as you like, but you won't get anywhere with it any more; you won't move it at all. I suppose it's because all the blood is clotting there. All we could do to cure it would be to cut my shoulder open and drain off all the bad blood. Please, Minakawa! Please, would you cut my shoulder open and take the blood off?"

"Don't be a fool," we replied as one man. "You need every drop of blood you've got, in your condition."

"No, if you don't get this bad blood away, my wind pipes'll get clogged up and I'll be done for. All you'd have to do would be to make a very small cut. Please—please, please do what I ask. Please cut it open and let the blood out; please...."

Umino was really crawling as he made this appeal to us.

"No, it's quite absurd, Umino. When you've eaten nothing but the miserable food we've been having for so long now, you'd die like a flash if you lost any blood. You must realise how precious every—"

"I realise, yes. But I can't stand it like this a minute longer. My breath's getting choked. Please, please, I'm asking you. Please cut me open and..." Umino was gasping for breath as he made this final appeal to us. In his eyes there burned a flashing earnestness that underlined his conviction that this was his only way of surviving. At length, he began to wear down our resolve.

"All right, then. But—and I'm really serious—I think we'd better make only the tiniest cut...." Minakawa was still trying to warn him how serious it would be for him to lose more than a few drops of blood.

Umino held out his razor, made from a piece of stainless steel, and, as he took it, Minakawa warned again, "Now, I'm only going to make the tiniest cut, remember."

As he stripped himself to the waist, Umino said, "Don't worry about me. Just get on with the cutting and don't give any thought to me."

"It won't do any good, this sort of thing. It just won't bring any benefit. Mark my words, no good at all will come

116

of it. . . ." Minakawa was chuntering away to himself, as he prepared at last to do what Umino wanted. First he let the razor blade sink gently and only very slightly into the flesh of the right shoulder: it was hard to find flesh, in fact, for the shoulder was reduced to an emaciated framework of skin and bone. A spurt of crimson blood flowed from the wan, white skin, and tricked down over Umino's breast.

"I should say that'd be just about enough," I said, swabbing the trickle of blood with a strip of rag as I spoke.

"No! More! Make a bigger cut! Don't think about me. Just take your courage in both hands and cut it bigger next time. Otherwise I'll suffocate before very long."

"But it must hurt, surely?" asked Minakawa, full of anxiety.

"No. It doesn't hurt one little bit. Make a much bigger cut, please. It won't do any good, a little scratch like that."

This time, with his hands trembling, Minakawa let the razor sink slightly further into the flesh and the blood came streaming out.

Just at this point, I noticed a sudden change in the colour of Umino's complexion. It seemed to me to have gone not so much wan and yellow as transparent and limpid. There was for an instant a movement of the bearded, ghastly face that showed signs of complete relief.

"Ah!—that feels tons better," Umino whispered as he heaved a long sigh. "Now for the left shoulder as well, please."

"No, we've done enough. Any more and that'd be the end of you. No—that's that for today, I think." We both of us refused, firmly, almost savagely.

But Umino would not listen to us. And as there was nothing else for it, I took the razor from Minakawa this time and gently sank the blade in Umino's left shoulder.

"Oh, that feels wonderful! I feel as if I'm alive again at long last!" Umino let his eyes creep up to meet ours, and managed a pale reflection of a smile. We swabbed the cuts

117

and bandaged them with strips of cloth. Then we got him off to sleep.

On the following day, Umino implored us to do it all over again. And worn down by his repeated pleas, we could do nothing but, very reluctantly, do as he asked.

After we'd drawn the blood, Umino went off into a doze, apparently very much more chirpy. But this didn't last very long and soon he was awake again, complaining of the stiffness in his shoulders and clamouring for us to draw off more blood. We took only the slightest drop this time and he said at once that he felt much better again and fell into a deep sleep.

This went on for two whole days.

Minakawa and I talked with each other and decided that Umino was beyond all the help we could give him. I felt black and gloomy, because I did want to help him some way or another, but we had nothing in the way of proper medicine. Apart from creosote, all we had was some eel's gallbladder which we had dried ourselves and which we used to dose ourselves whenever our stomachs or our bowels went upset. So there was absolutely nothing we could do for him.

On the eighth of July (I think it was in 1954) we neither of us left Umino's side for a single minute.

In the early evening he seemed suddenly to regain a little energy and he started to jabber away about all kinds of things. He prattled away, hardly stopping for breath, about Shimizu in Shizuoka, about Mount Fuji, about his grandfather, about everything under the sun: there was all the pride in his home town and his part of Japan that there had been when we used to talk together during the early years while he still had his health.

After a while, he said suddenly, "God! It's hot! It's so hot, I could do with a water-pillow."

I went straight off to fill our inner tube and as I propped his head on it, he said, "Ah! I've suddenly gone very sleepy..." and with that he promptly shut his eyes. "If I

118

could get a really sound sleep, it could well ease things a bit for me," he murmured.

We crept quietly back to our own shelters and lay down. But there was not a hope of getting off to sleep.

Night fell early among the dense jungle trees, and it was already beginning to grow dark.

I heard a noise like the scamper of a wood-mouse and turned my head so that I could see what was going on outside. The dim shadow of Minakawa was moving silently and swiftly in the direction of Umino's cave. I thought I would go as well and see how Umino was, and I was just getting to my knees when I heard Minakawa calling to me.

"Itō! Itō!" His voice was frantic.

My heart stood still as I wondered what had happened. With just socks on my feet, for I didn't stop even to put my shoes on, I leaped across to Umino's shelter. Minakawa was kneeling by Umino's head, looking down solemnly at his face.

"Gone!"

Minakawa lifted his eyes to look at me as he said this one word, then he again lowered his gaze to Umino's face, which had already changed completely and bore the stamp of death.

"It looks as if he couldn't stand all that blood being taken from him, after all," I murmured, grasping the hand of the dead man.

"No, it wasn't anything to do with that; don't worry. His number was up already when he found his way back to us, and that's for sure." Minakawa never let his eyes leave Umino's face; he seemed to be trying to convince himself, and he spoke absently in a husky whisper, the words coming out very slowly.

I bit my lips, to keep back my emotions. I kept trying to tell myself that it was the war that had killed Umino, and the very thought left a taste of lead in my mouth.

That night, we draped a sheet of tenting over Umino's dead body and kept vigil by his side until the daylight returned. As I sat by the cold, still corpse, I remembered the time when I had quarrelled with Umino and we had come to blows. And once that memory was revived, I couldn't stop it floating backwards and forwards, time after time, across my mind.

"What time would you say it was when he stopped breathing?" I had to break the awful silence, and I asked the question hoping to fetch up these murky thoughts and get rid of them along with my words.

"It looks as if it was pretty soon after we'd left him," Minakawa replied. "When I came across to see how he was, he was already quite cold."

If I choose to think back to Umino's shelter even now, I can still feel that coldness in my palm today.

We had always been told that one should not bury a body until twenty-four hours after the time of death, so we didn't stir from Umino's side until it was getting near the evening of the following day.

Minakawa used to have a small image of the Buddha carved in wood which he always carried next to his skin. This he enshrined in Umino's shelter for the vigil and for the period while we were going through the last rites for the dead man.

Minakawa said once that this little image of the Buddha had no doubt belonged to a Japanese soldier. He told me that he had picked it up once in front of a cave, during the time before we met up and joined forces. It was no more than three inches high at the outside, and was carved in relief out of a piece of ordinary wood.

In the afternoon of the day after our vigil, we set about laying out Umino's body. We shaved off his beard, and did his hair, which must have been all of two feet long, into a neat bun. Among his effects, we discovered some garments which you could call new and which must have come into his possession during the period while he was living on his own, so we clothed him in these. As we bared his shoulders we noticed that the scars of the incisions we had made, all to no purpose, had now turned to jet-black scabs. We got Umino thoroughly clean and purified and then dug a hole for his tomb nearby. After only a shallow layer of soil, we came to a rock bed, so it took a great deal of hard labour to get as far as two feet or so down. Umino didn't have all that many possessions—perhaps because he was never very strong from the first—and we had no difficulty in packing all he had with his body in the grave. As we began to put the earth back over him, my feelings again became too much for me, so much so that I broke down completely.

As soon as we had finished filling up the grave, we moved our shelter about two hundred yards away, so that we should not have Umino always brought to mind whenever we looked around ourselves.

Relations between Umino and me had never been of the best: we often quarrelled and never quite saw eye to eye. But now he would never be seen on this earth again, try how I might, I was quite unable to stifle a terrible sense of shame....

14

What Kept Life Going

If one were to think for a moment of the results of Umino's death, I am sure the answer would be bound to be in terms of the deepening of the bond of affection between the two of us whom he left alive.

We practically never talked to each other, almost as though we had forgotten that such things as words existed. Except when it was absolutely vital to pass on information, we lived in a shared silence brimming with empathy. But I could not shake myself free from feeling as if a vacuum as big as the world had taken the place of my heart. And I suspect that Minakawa felt much the same.

But somehow we had to live on; we had to put our all into the task of survival. For me, it was Minakawa and Minakawa alone who made this possible; for me he filled the vacuum. And, if you asked Minakawa his views, I have no doubt he'd say that I did exactly the same for him.

It was precisely because we were each able, little by little, to fill up this vacuum for the other that we were able to pass safely through the abyss of what may well have been the most precarious period of our entire sixteen years in the jungle. And no doubt this stemmed, in the last analysis, from the commonsense realisation on the part of each of us that, if the other were to die, he himself could not survive alone.

It was just after this trying period that we began to talk to each other about God. I reckoned that Minakawa's was one way of life—the way he seemed to sustain himself by faith; but I also reckoned that my own irreligious, atheistic outlook could be considered a way of life just as valid. If a man believed in a Shinto deity (or the Buddha), then such Beings existed—for him; if he didn't believe, then they did not exist. My idea was that a man was free to choose for himself, and that his choice was something quite beyond the scope of any other's comprehension.

Minakawa was tolerant towards these ideas of mine; in exactly the same way, I thought him a fine example of a man, in spite of his always keeping next to his skin the image of the Buddha which he had found in a cave, or as many as twenty different sorts of charms from Shinto shrines or Buddhist temples back home in Japan which he had come across as he roamed the jungle. I have said I thought him a fine example of a man; and I still think so—the finest I have ever met.

Life eventually began to run again along the old tracks, and we started to spend our days walking the jungle, scouring it from end to end. But Umino's death still affected us curiously and we found that some of the old questing spirit had gone. Once we had gathered enough food to last us for two or three days, we lost all enthusiasm and set off back then and there for our hiding place. On one such day when we were out foraging, we had just come off a slope and reached a narrow, level area when, to our surprise and alarm, we heard something crashing through the scrub at us! We cowered down in the undergrowth, not daring to move. A second or two afterwards, a pig trundled past, a mere two or three yards away from us, nosing the ground with its snout all the time as it passed!

I didn't have my gun with me that day and, somehow, I could raise no spirit to give chase to it.

"It's the way of a wild animal always to use the same track. If we were to wait here, we'd be able to have a shot at nabbing him. What do you say?"—thus Minakawa, once we had got over our surprise.

"Yes, that's all very well; but I'd guess he started out in life as a domestic pig—I shouldn't imagine we'd be able to repeat anything like our efforts with the stag," I objected.

"Oh, rubbish! You're forgetting he'll have been roaming the hills these last ten years and more. That'll have turned him as wild an animal as you could wish for." Minakawa spoke with a force that was new to him.

So we searched around for boulders large enough for our purpose, and when we had found them—they must have weighed all of twenty or thirty pounds—we each lugged one up a tree and lay in wait there for the pig to return. The plan was simply to let the boulders fall on the animal's head as he passed.

We hid ourselves in the thick foliage for the remainder of that day. No pig. So we got down from the tree, hid our boulders by its roots, and made our way back to our shelters.

At crack of dawn the following morning, we set off for the same spot and, cradling our rocks in anticipation, we waited all day again up the tree; but not a sign of the pig!

"The blessed thing only came this way by chance after all, you see. It *wasn't* its regular route. I told you so, didn't

123

I?" I couldn't miss this chance of letting Minakawa know how right I'd been.

"I'm afraid I don't know," Minakawa replied ambiguously to my outburst. "All I can say is, I think we shouldn't give it up quite so readily. After all, we've only been here yesterday and today. I'll tell you what—let's have another go tomorrow; if we find we've had another day's wait for nothing by tomorrow night, then I'll agree you were right and that it was just the odd pig that lost its way. But we won't call off the hunt till tomorrow night. Right?"

The following morning—in that this was to see our last attempt—we set out even earlier than before. We climbed our tree, boulders and all—and we'd only just got ourselves in position when we heard a fearsome clatter and a crashing from the scrub! And then there was the distinctive nasal snort that could only come from a pig foraging for food. . . .

Hurriedly and in great excitement we lifted our boulder-bombs and steadied them with both hands, waiting for the right moment. We had it all worked out that I should aim at the pig's head, Minakawa for its spine. Through the leaves of the scrub, I had a fleeting glance of something whitish. I let the boulder go, and heard a squeal of anguish. I skimmed down the tree in a flash. The pig was squealing blue murder: my boulder had knocked it over on to its side and its legs were pawing the air. I picked up the stone and crashed it down once more on the pig—on its skull just above the right ear. And that was that for Mr. Pig.

We set to work tearing the meat off the carcass there and then. We buried the hide, the bones, the intestines and the head. We strewed dry leaves over the freshly turned earth so that we left no signs of the slaughter. We took the fat for lard and the rest of the meat we carried to the cave where we stored our most prized possessions; it was salted and stored away in the shell-case. We then wrapped in a piece of rag only as much as we should eat that evening, and took it back with us to our shelters.

That night, we sampled the first salted pork *sukiyaki* we'd either of us eaten for many a long year.

Three or four years later we got our second pig by the same methods.

15

Knowing How To Survive

We had got a good stock of pork pickled in salt—enough for two or three months' subsidiary diet—but, as a result, we found ourselves faced with a shortage of salt far earlier than we had anticipated.

Once we had learned how to make salt, we had got into the habit of taking advantage of the dry season every year and giving over all our energies to making and laying in a stock. We had discovered that, by and large, five trips to the coast to collect sea water provided us with enough salt to last us the year out. We found that we could get just over a couple of pints of salt from our tire inner tube filled with sea water. So, if we collected five inner tubes'-worth of sea water, this gave us about a gallon and a half of salt—equivalent to the amount needed by a human body in the space of a year.

However, we gambled with our lives every time we went to collect sea water, and this task caused us more fatigue and anguish—both physical and mental—than all the others put together.

At first, the hazards and the adventures of sea water collecting and carrying did not put us out unduly as far as the mere physical aspect was concerned; and, discounting for a moment the sores made by the tin can as it chafed against your back, there was precious little reaction. It certainly didn't require anything of the level of five or six days of lying low and sleeping it off to regain our energies.

But by now it had become an undertaking of a very different order. Agreed, our inner tube made no noise, and you could say without fear of contradiction that it was pretty nearly the ideal container for lumping sea water: however, even if you disregard the increasing mental strain occasioned by the risk of possible discovery by aboriginals or by Americans, from the physical point of view it was now a terribly formidable task, demanding heavy work which became the more difficult to stand up to the more our physical powers of resistance ebbed. There's room for a lot of water in a truck tube; and it's heavy!

As a result, on days when we were going out after sea water, Minakawa and I grew more and more into the habit of talking at length about our physical condition before we set off. If we hadn't first convinced each other that there did exist in us the assurance and the faith that would enable us to stand up to these heavy labours, we could never have set out with the sort of control and carefree abandon that the escapade required. You see, we had to think ourselves into an awareness that, if we did once collapse during the operation, there could be no hope of getting back alive.

It was for this reason that we now made it a regular habit to move our shelter during the dry season to a site which, while being as near as possible to the coast, was still in the hill jungle zone where it would not attract attention. Our physical condition itself imposed a limit of no more than two thousand yards between our shelter and the coastline— we could just not make the journey if it were more. And a lower limit of twelve hundred or thirteen hundred yards or so was set by the nature of the ground itself—we would be far too conspicuous if we settled down any nearer to the sea than that. And in spite of this comparatively short distance (for a man in full vigour, that is), after just one trip to collect sea water we were obliged to abandon all thought of work—by which I mean foraging for food—for as long as a whole week. This practice, in fact, continued right up to the time when we were eventually taken by the Americans.

I have already outlined how we timed our movements when we were out on a sea water-gathering operation. We would start to move in the early evening and, once arrived at the cliff which marked the edge of the jungle, we would wait for it to get completely dark before we went down to the coast. I repeat it here as I must make it quite clear how, even on this part of the journey, it was a matter of sheer chance whether or not we were discovered by aboriginals or Americans. Then we'd have to cross the made-up road, fill our inner tube with sea water, and, before first light, get ourselves laid up in the scrub below the coconut grove which bordered the road. Part of the reason for hiding up here was to save our strength, though the principal motive was so that we could wait until the following night, when we could again move without too much fear of detection.

You can tell how much these expeditions cost us in the way of physical exertion when I say that *it took as much as twenty and sometimes even forty days' rest before we were anywhere near recovered from our exhaustion!* However, we just couldn't find a way to spare ourselves this chore.

If you once fell ill, there was nothing for it but to try and lie up quietly in your shelter and hope to sleep it off. All you could do was wait patiently for nature and your physical state to take a turn for the better. So there were times when you went without food for several days on end. You felt just like a wild animal that has been winged, cowering silently in the cover of the jungle scrub, with only your ears and eyes to help you, just waiting and hoping against hope that something would turn up, that something would take it all off your shoulders. This "something", for some people, I suppose, would be God; for me, with my outlook on life, it was probably my will to live. Nothing would come of lifting your voice and bewailing and cursing your fate at this juncture. All you could do, all that the circumstances permitted you to do, was simply to wait it out calmly and quietly.

In such ways, we gradually acquired the know-how of staying alive: bit by bit we lost our powers of rational thought and came to increase the intuitive sensitivity of our conditioned reflexes.

We allowed our hair to grow naturally and learnt how to bind it into a neat topknot. And we made a variety of tools and items of equipment from other people's (usually the Americans') refuse: we made ourselves razors, for example, mosquito nets and clothes; and we had mastered the art of making fire with wire rope, wood and gunpowder.

In the plainlands around us, we knew very well that there were men driving cars or trucks, flirting with women, listening to music, going to see films, but this was a world that we were not allowed to go near or enter. Sometimes, maddeningly, we could hear their voices among the trees.

We would go to our crag after sunset and peep down from it on the people living in the so-called "melting pot of civilisation"; down there, we knew, men and women were allowed to live together, allowed to make love, their lips touching, their legs and bodies clinging and intertwined. But we were mere onlookers; we were allowed no part in any of it. We were like a pair of rats, peering through a hole in a broken-down wall and gazing longingly and intently at the life of the human being, eyes and ears tuned to the utmost point of sensitivity. At any moment, a horrible and fearful cat might appear out of the blue, come bearing down on us and grab us by the throat; somewhere or other, someone might have left poisoned food for us.

Who were the swines who had forced us to become such "jungle rats"?

However, we "rats", as the months and years passed, gained a deeper know-how of our new form of life. There were times, for example, when we could tell, from the smell of tobacco even, that someone was getting too near us for comfort, and we were able to hide ourselves away in the scrub safely and successfully. Again, often when we were out in the jungle, we would come upon other people's tracks leading through the scrub; whenever this happened, we used to take a bitchy delight in deliberately blocking these tracks with shrubs and branches. If an aboriginal used such tracks, he would be quite unable to get past this barrier unless he chopped it all away; otherwise, he would have to make a troublesome detour.

But it required a great deal of planning and scheming before this sort of approach had become a part of our nature. If anything unnatural or unusual were recognisable about our "barrier" the next time we passed by, then this would be convincing proof that other human beings had been there. And in our eyes, remember, as rats, all other human beings were cats. We would always avoid using a second time any track where we had left this sort of booby trap.

We often wondered what would happen to our faith—whatever the Beings or entities we believed in—by the time we got to the point when the know-how of survival became a sort of second nature to us. But we need not have given it a moment's worry, for we had found our way back again into the civilised world before this could happen.

16

Bullets and Barbarian Choppers

It was raining cats and dogs.

We were living at the time on the hill to which we had given the name "Coconut Palm Mount". It was now getting on for a couple of months since the rainy season had set in. The year was 1957.

We had built ourselves a shelter slightly different from the previous models. We had two separate sheets of tenting slung up at just about head height, and we had left a space of getting on for two feet between them. In the ground between these two "tents"—if you could give the name to such primitive efforts—we had built a small, joint cooking-stove. This new style of shelter was so planned that we were able each to live in our own section while still using the same stove simultaneously, and still being able to carry on a conversation. It had become too much like hard work to have to go out every time we wished to speak!

That day it had been raining hard since the early morning, so we had started in to a light and leisurely breakfast. We sat cross-legged, facing each other across the stove, and talked in voices that were no louder than the din made by the rain as it beat down on our tents.

"I can't *really* believe it; but I keep on feeling that the war might perhaps be over...."

"Maybe you're right; maybe it *is* all over. I haven't a clue which side won if it is; but it could just be that those leaflets and that letter weren't fakes after all."

"All the same, if we get careless and show ourselves, we're pretty sure to get picked off by some aboriginal. If the war really was over, why should there still be shooting going on, do you think?"

"It could be there's still fighting going on here somewhere."

"You don't really think so, do you? No! It's thirteen years since the Americans landed! It can't be, surely?"

"Do you think perhaps the Americans living down on the plains have set a price on the heads of all us Japanese soldiers?"

"I don't know. I just don't know." Minakawa repeated the words, an element that was part helpless groan, part cry of distress in them.

"If that is what's happened, we're doomed, are we, to live in these hills till we die?" I raised my voice as I asked the question.

"I should say there's precious little hope, now, of us ever getting back to Japan alive. The island crawls with Americans, and they've got us completely surrounded. If they got hold of us, we'd be their prisoners. And you know what our officers always used to say about being a prisoner in

130

American hands: they're all killed, they said, didn't they?"

"If the war *was* over, the aboriginals wouldn't still be slaughtering us like pigs, would they? That's a thought, isn't it? And if I'm right, then maybe the war's still going on after all."

"There's something else, though; if it wasn't, surely you wouldn't see so many American soldiers having such a high time fooling around with tarts and all that?"

"I dreamed about my father last night." I had been silent for a while, and now tried a new subject for a fresh approach. "He was sitting round the hearth just like us, and drinking bean-paste soup. It was hot and he was blowing on it. I don't suppose we shall ever have the chance of tasting dear old bean-paste soup again, shall we?"

"No. . . . If we're never going to be able to get out of this jungle, then it stands to reason we're never going to set eyes on bean-paste soup again. Still . . ."

With this, there was a further break in the conversation. Minakawa flung himself over on his side and I, too, turned away and lay on my back, pondering how I could set the talk going again; but I felt there was just no seed that would sprout a conversation.

The rain kept on drumming on the tenting, and the noise dinned in my ears. Soon this sound began to harmonise with the splatter of the drops on the leaves, and it seemed almost as if I was listening to a concerto, as the whole hill around me was battered into voice by the downpour. Presently, the sounds grew weaker, as if they were being swallowed up and absorbed by the earth, and, in the end, all the noise seemed to have been dulled and to have evaporated, as if one were living in a soundless world on the bed of the sea. . . .

Suddenly a noise of quite a different character jerked me rudely out of my daydreams. It was the kind of noise that you don't so much hear as *absorb* with your nervous system. Like a flash, my gaze sped in the direction from which the sound had come. In a thousandth of a second, my eye took in a succession of linked images—the hat, the face of the Chamorro tribesman, the gun, the trousers, the bare feet.

I forgot all about the noise we always made as a warning signal (it sounded something like *chyut*) and, jerking myself to my feet with a scream of, *"They're here!"*, I leaped out into the rain. For a split second, the "barbarian chopper" slipped into my field of vision. I stretched out one hand to make a grab for it, and it was just in that same instant that I heard the gun being fired.

Only the single shot but I could feel the report crunch through my whole system more noisily than any bomb blast I'd ever heard! Then I felt a burning pain in my back. But by now I was already ducking down the scrub-covered slope in the opposite direction. And I burst down that slope with the force and impetus of a rolling boulder.

By the time I'd got some hold of myself, I found I was already a good half way down the hill. And there I discovered the hut of some aboriginal—and was promptly assailed by another quite distinct fear. I stopped on the instant, set off again at a tangent, and forced my way rapidly another fifty yards down the slope.

We had never dreamed that there might be aboriginals living so near to us.

There was another gun report—again, only one shot. And then Minakawa was standing by me. From the glance he gave me, I must have stared at him for a moment as though I had never seen him before....

"You all right?"

The words jerked me back to my senses, and I felt the smarting pain in my back. I rolled up my shirt tail and turned so that Minakawa could see my back.

"My God, you were lucky! It's only grazed you. Is this the lot? Nowhere else?"

"No: that's the lot."

"Well, he only grazed you then."

"That was an aboriginal." As I spoke, I squatted down in

the thick scrub alongside Minakawa. It was comforting to have him just by my side again.

"He was barefoot. He was no hunter."

"He could have been a mountain guard, I suppose."

"Yes, a mountain guard, maybe; taking a look round his sector—and we never realised." Minakawa peeped out through the thick scrub as he spoke.

"It was a dangerous place to choose for a shelter, wasn't it?"

"It was, with a vengeance! You were lucky to come out of it with only a grazing, you know."

There was a very serious note in Minakawa's voice as he whispered these words. He put some paper over my wound, and on top of that he tied a sort of belly-band bandage with a strip of cloth which I always carried on me in place of a towel.

We had no medicines or ointments for such wounds. Usually, we treated and cured grazes of this sort by licking them. It was just what an animal would have done. However, you couldn't lick your back, and all I could do was to wait for it to heal naturally. If, in an unguarded moment, I got river water or even rain on it, and it began to fester, it could turn into something serious.

"Oh, Hell! Now we shall have all the bother of moving our shelters again, shan't we?" Minakawa spoke as if he'd only just bethought himself of this. I nodded without saying anything.

For two or three hours we didn't stir an inch. We realised only too well that if we moved without great care and caution, we should increase the risk of discovery.

Eventually we started at a very slow pace. The rain still beat down in torrents, spattering on the ground and swamping the leaves around us. I was glad to let Minakawa take the lead and we set off climbing the slope once more.

We got as far as a point from which we could see our shelters, then we halted again so that we could have a final check to make sure it was quite safe to go on. We lay stock still, like cats poised to make a dart at their prey, but there wasn't a sign of a soul there, so we went into our shelters and busied ourselves at once with preparations for the move. With the least possible waste of time and energy, we got our luggage ready and set off again down the same slope that the man from the hill patrol had climbed to attack us. As we walked, there was a terrible stab of pain from my back wound; it felt now almost as if the wound had gone very deep into my flesh.

We made our way down the slope, across a valley with a stream running through it, and then climbed a hill on the other side. At the top of the hill we paused to take in the view; there was range after range of hills, as far as the eye could see, rising and falling like a procession of waves on the sea, and each of them was covered with dense scrub. Behind us the jungle ended at the bluff dropping to the inhabited coastal strip.

We picked out one of the nearer hills and built ourselves low shelters half-way up its slope.

The wound in my back healed completely after about a week. There was only the scar to show for it, oval-shaped and no bigger than the tip of your little finger. "My God, though, how dangerous it could have been," exclaimed Minakawa, as he took a look at the scar. "It'd only have needed to be an inch or two to one side, and it would have meant the end for you, I bet."

"I've got a feeling it was my sticking out my hand to grab at the 'barbarian chopper' that made the bullet glance off. If I hadn't noticed the 'chopper' in the split second and if, instead of going for it, I'd flung myself out of the shelter straight away, it's quite likely the bullet would have torn its way right through my back from left to right, as the other one did with Miyazawa." I shuddered.

"You're absolutely right. And if you'd bought it, what about me? I'd have lost all the will and all the strength it takes to keep going. I'd not have been able to survive."

I held my tongue—I, too, had had much the same thought.

Supposing it had been Minakawa who'd been the target, and supposing he'd stopped the bullet instead of me—it might well have been that I, too, would have lost all the will to stay alive. For, although we were two separate lives, in fact, the two were inter-twined and mutually dependent. The relationship was analagous to that between two columns supporting a pediment—and each other thereby. Once one of the columns falls, the other tumbles to the ground with it.

The realisation of this fact set us talking and vowing once more to each other that we would be that little bit more cautious in the future and would set even greater store by the life that we held so intimately in common.

17

Youth Slipping By

It was a pretty general rule that I fell ill two or three times a year. I don't know what caused this illness, but, though it laid me up and meant taking to my bed, it wasn't all that serious; it wasn't enough to cause screams of pain or make life really unbearable.

Once, while I was forced to rest up by one of these attacks, I began to carve a figure of a nude woman, using as my model a photograph of an American woman in a magazine that I had discovered in the American army rubbish tip.

For my carving implements, I used the same small edged tool with which I made my seals, our "barbarian chopper", and a kitchen-knife.

The woman in the photograph had a beautiful face. Her shoulders, her breasts, and her hips were sinewy, but sinewy in a pretty and an attractive way. She was in western-style clothes and from her laugh, which looked to be quite natural and unforced, I would have said she had a pleasant personality.

Time after time, in my mind, I took that woman's clothes off until she stood stark naked in front of me.

Then I would prop the photo up and do my best to reproduce what my mind's eye could see in the foot-high carving. Off came the clothes, one by one; and at the end, there she stood, modelling for me and very beautiful in her nakedness. This little play-act of mine, I found, gave me a diversion and a consolation that nothing else could. The model girl stood there in front of me, that lovely, natural smile always on her face. All I needed to do was look greedily at her, help her off with her clothes, strip her quite bare—and I felt absolutely fine!

I found that, if you looked at the photograph from one side, you could follow a line down from the woman's shoulders and get in a crafty glance at the bulge of her breasts. You had to use your imagination a bit, but I was good at that—and found myself getting better, too! Then you went on a bit further from there: they looked lovely firm and full breasts, and I found myself imagining that I was getting my hand in and holding it gently over the milky, smooth skin. And once I had got the photo reproduced in my little carving, it got easier and easier. The girl in the photo, you see, wouldn't let me have a look at her stomach or her hips or her thighs—somehow I had always pictured them as lovely, fleshy thighs. But all I had to do was use my powers of instinct, and there they would be, given full expression, one by one, in my carving. As a result, once I had got my carving tool in my hand and I was working away happily, I found I could forget myself completely.

Now and again, Minakawa gave me the odd suggestion— and bits of advice. "You have to remember," he said loftily, "that I'm a man of experience. Don't forget, I was married before I joined up. That's where you and I differ, Itō. If it's anything to do with women, then I am your senior by a long chalk!"

Minakawa, in fact, did a lot to spur my powers of imagination, and he told me a great deal that I had never realised about the world of women. And the more he told me, the more the feeling grew that the springtime of my youth, spent here in the jungle, was being poured out wastefully and seeping uselessly into the ground. And once it had drained away, had been sucked to the bowels of the earth, there was no way of recalling it.

The woman in the photograph was gradually being given expression in front of our eyes, in all her luscious naked-ness. On the day I put the finishing touches to her, we decked out the nude figure—which was barely a foot high, you remember—and, hardly able to shift our eyes from it for a second, we began to talk sex.

This figure of the woman seemed now to have slipped beyond the influence and control of my hands, and there she was standing in front of our very eyes taking on all the qualities of an actual live human being....

"You've got the line of the hips damned well, I think." Minakawa had set her up so that her back was to him. He spoke in a judicious tone.

"No. I like the breasts best of all. They seem to be really alive, somehow."

"That's because you've never had a real woman, you know." As he spoke, Minakawa turned the naked figure round to face us. Pictures and memories of the girls back home in the village flashed through my mind. But they were all blurred, and not one of them would come clear and vivid enough to satisfy my imagination. The only ones at all clear—and then it was only the faces—were my own little sister and Aihara's sister. And neither of them would grow up. I kept visualising them, of course, as I had last seen them. Besides—sisters are sisters; and as for the image of Aihara's, I kept on seeing the figure of my dead friend, in my mind's eye, at her side!

My trouble was that there just didn't exist, in my heart or in my memory, anything which you could call "woman" in

137

the true sense of the word. But this nude whom I'd discovered and created with my own hands now had the freedom of both. As I stared at her, this one-foot-high thing with a body made of wood became transformed into a living woman, with blood and flesh and a smooth and silky skin. So much so that there were times when I even felt that the springtime of my youth had been built into and was impregnating this carving.

I made other nude carvings later to act as older and younger sisters to my first woman, and the result of it all was, without doubt, that these nude female forms did sow within us the seeds of vital youthful stirrings long forgotten.

We came to spend time "talking" with these women, about the mysteries of sex and the secrets of a woman. Whenever we were forced to move our hiding place, our practice was to confine our wooden harem for a short period in a secret cave. Then, when we had got our new hiding place all ship-shape, we would go and collect them, and they would once again be given a home—a home in a shelter encircled by tenting, weeds and leaves. And, restored to their rightful place in this home, they would once again join in our conversations about the war, our home towns, food and sex.

18

Under "Triangle Heights"

We had the impression that the patrols were not quite so regular and strict as they had been. "It could well be that there are no other Japanese soldiers left alive on Guam," we used to say to each other.

For one thing, although we ranged quite widely through the jungle, there were far less frequent signs of a patrol;

moreover, we now never fell in with any other Japanese stragglers. In fact, we came to believe that, after Umino's death, we really were the last survivors in the jungle.

Some time previously, Minakawa had started to complain of not being able to see in the dark. "Looks as though I've gone and got night-blindness," he said calmly, trying to see what was going on about him.

It seemed that he was right. Whereas in the dark I was able to see a distance of almost thirty yards, Minakawa could hardly recognise a thing from the moment the sun began to go down.

"They do say, don't they, that eels are good for night-blindness?" Minakawa had evidently bethought himself of the old story that had become a common piece of lore in Japan: that lampreys are one of the best cures for this condition.

Minakawa really began to get a "thing" about fish. He would keep on muttering, "I'd love some raw fish: I'd love some raw fish..."—almost as if some demon had got hold of him. However, the plain fact was that we couldn't even lay hands on a single sardine to make into a raw fish for him.

We used to go out at sunset or at crack of dawn to the middle reaches of the river Talofofo. This was the place where I'd often gone out fishing for eels while all was still well with the Company and the Battalion.

The eels didn't give us all that much trouble. Once, beaming gleefully at the sight of a large one we'd just that minute taken, Minakawa said, "We'll make him into *sashimi*" (a raw fish dish) "and stick some salt on him, and he'll be ever so tasty."

I felt constrained to sound the voice of caution. "It's not at all safe to eat raw food, remember. If I were you, I think I'd pack it in. You'd do far better to cook it before you eat it, if you ask me." As I spoke, I got busy dressing an eel that was as long and thick as my arm. I ripped open the belly— and shoved the creature away from me in disgust. It was positively swarming with hundreds and thousands of parasites inside....

"Good heavens! Minakawa! Just take a look at this! Eat this sort of thing raw and you could kill yourself. You can be as fond as you like of your eels—but it's much more important to watch your health."

And Minakawa seemed as if he, too, was pretty shaken.

So all we did with that particular eel was take out its gallbladder, dry it, and make it into medicine for stomach troubles. And we found, after this unfortunate experience, that neither of us could ever quite bring ourselves to touch an eel again!

We were very scrupulous about observing the old health precept—"never fill your belly more than four-fifths full"; in other words, to be moderate in our eating habits. Minakawa, whose stomach was not of the strongest, was particularly careful to keep to this rule.

Although there wasn't any particular ailment that we could actually point to, we were in fact now finding that our powers—mental as well as physical—were gradually failing; I could no longer concentrate on things, really ferret something out, and it took more and more out of me, for instance, to carry anything heavy for more than the shortest distance. There was one particular kind of ailment, and we were never able to find the cause of it, that made you so run-down that you suffered a good month of terrible lassitude, when all you wanted to do, or could manage to do, was mooch around droopily and sleep in fits and starts.

After he'd started to complain about his night-blindness, Minakawa used to go down, once a year on the average, with some sort of attack like this that brought him really low, and made him terribly listless. With this sort of thing to fight, he was even more scrupulous to follow his "four-fifths rule": even if we'd shot a cow, even if we'd been blessed with the luck of a rich haul of prawns, he'd still be very careful about rash over-eating, and all left-overs he would pickle in salt and store up for future reference.

In this way we did our best to minimise the cumulative effects of malnutrition which our privations imposed upon us.

We had finished our hazardous sea-water-collecting epic, one year, and had had about a week's rest. This had gone some way towards assisting our recuperation. The wet season was coming round again and it was almost time for us to begin preparations for our regular move at this part of the season.

It was again the difficult transition period as far as our staple food went, while we were switching from "rose potatoes" to breadfruit.

"Itō! We're catching that chicken today...." These were Minakawa's first words of the day, uttered the very moment his eyes opened. The bird was one we'd caught a glimpse of among the trees the night before.

We had a breakfast of unpalatable and uninspiring "rose potato" and we then made our way towards the glade where we'd spotted the chicken. There was not a sign of him, of course. "We missed our chance with him, all right. There'll be no catching him now, you know." I was for packing it in and getting back home.

"Oh, come on! Give it a chance. Let's just have one more look for him." Minakawa clearly couldn't bring himself to give up the search as easily as this.

"A bit of chicken—yes, I agree with you; very tasty. But if we over-strained ourselves and wrecked our health, that would be the end."

I hadn't managed yet to shake off entirely the weariness that had followed our sea-water-gathering expeditions, and, as a result, I just couldn't summon enough enthusiasm—or energy—to go on with the hunt. "I'm sorry," I said, almost weeping. "I feel so bloody weary and worn-out..."

"All right, then. There's an end to it as far as you're concerned—you'd better get back to the shelter and get the weight off your feet." Minakawa sounded anxious about my condition. "I can manage very well on my own. I'll get

141

him—you see!—and, in the meanwhile, you take yourself back to have a rest. Anyway, whatever happens about the chicken, I must have some breadfruit myself. These bloody 'rose potatoes' aren't doing my digestion any good at all, so I'm going to try for some early ones. . . ."

I apologised again, left him, and dragged myself back to the shelter.

I couldn't bring myself to think about or concentrate on anything at all. I had the feeling that, somehow, it was all going to be the same whether I tried to think things out or just let it all slide. The empty feeling in my stomach as I lay under the tenting set up a tickle around my throat, but I couldn't raise the energy even to lift myself up and do anything about it. Still lying full length, I stretched out a hand for the naked figure of the American woman. It was now soiled with dirty fingermarks. I kept turning her round, gazing at her from every possible angle.

Later, I suddenly realised it seemed a long time since Minakawa and I had parted company. And this was odd, as we had lately agreed not to stray too far from the shelter, when we were acting independently. We never went more than two hours' journey away—yet it must be all of three since I saw Minakawa. What had happened to him?

"Time he was back," I said to myself. "He's late."

I started to glance through the American magazine that I'd picked up in the rubbish tip. And, as always, it was the photograph of the woman that my eye rested on, the photograph that I'd looked at hundreds—no, it must by now have been thousands!—of times.

Presently, from the angle of the shafts of light from the sun penetrating the dense scrub, I knew it must be pretty near mid-day. "He's really late now," I realised. "I don't see how he *can* have missed the way. No—but what can have happened to make him so late?"

I began to get worried about Minakawa and soon I could think of nothing else but him. I was worried about him and yet I felt he would soon be back; and I found myself alternating between the two moods of anxiety and confidence. One minute, panic was uppermost, in the next, I was buoyed up with the expectation that he would be back on the instant.

"I'll wait just a *little* bit longer," I thought to myself for the umpteenth time.

I had a bite to eat. Then I concentrated all my faculties on the surroundings of the shelter, so that I could catch the smallest sound and sign of Minakawa returning. "I suppose it could just be that he fell down a tree and hurt his leg or something"—my mind was plagued with all kinds of ominous fears—"*Oh, God! Whatever can have happened to him?*"

I began to imagine worse and worse things, and, in the end, unable to wait for him any longer, I set out from the shelter. "Surely he can't have wandered miles away chasing his god-damned chicken?" I thought to myself crossly as I reached the area of the scrub where Minakawa and I had separated earlier that morning.

I looked at the shadows cast by the leaves of a huge tree. "Just as I feared," I told myself. "It's already past two o'clock." My misgivings increased with every moment that passed.

Suddenly I had an idea and set off in the direction of a special copse of trees which I knew always ripened the earliest of any in this particular area. As I walked, I realised how disturbed and troubled my thoughts were.

I began to search the part of the scrub where there was the highest possible concentration of breadfruit trees, making our tongue-clicking noises all the time. Beyond this patch of scrub lay the road with its occasional traffic.

"S's! S's!"

"T'sst! T'sst!"

I used both our warning signals, and, catlike, I edged nearer and nearer to a much more hazardous point: the other road which led from the east coast. We knew that this part was rich in breadfruit and coconut, and I wondered if Minakawa had been tempted by them.

However, it was far too optimistic to expect to be able to find any breadfruit fit to pick as early as May.

Still, Minakawa was fixed in his preference for breadfruit —with his weak stomach it was much easier on the digestion than "rose potatoes", and, in any case, had a far more pleasant taste. So I could imagine him venturing into an area even as risky as this in an attempt to get his hands on some.

I took all the precautions I could: I bent my body as I moved, I made our warning signals, and I never moved more than five or six paces at a time. Thus I made my way noiselessly through the scrub and got to a point where, only a hundred yards or so ahead of me, I should come out on the road.

I was scrutinising the bases of the trunks and the roots of all the breadfruit trees and coconut palms, because I imagined Minakawa might well have slipped from a tall branch and hurt his legs or his feet in a fall.

Presently, after I'd scoured the area underneath heaven knows how many trees, I came upon a rucksack and a pair of sandals. I needed no second glance to confirm that they belonged to Minakawa.

They were right underneath a coconut palm.

I went to pick them up and then suddenly noticed that the ground beside them was covered with leaves that had not long fallen. There could have been little doubt that Minakawa had gone after coconuts and had climbed this tree. I made our warning signal, and strained my ears to catch a reply. Nothing disturbed the silence.

By now I was full of apprehension that Minakawa had hurt himself really seriously and was lying unconscious somewhere, so I made a systematic search under every single tree in the whole area. However, apart from the sandals and the rucksack, the search yielded absolutely nothing.

In the end, some time after the sun had gone down, I decided reluctantly that I had better put it all off until the following day and made my way back to the shelter.

Back home, I started imagining the worst: could he have been discovered by a patrol and shot dead? No, this was hardly on the cards, since I hadn't heard the sound of a shot being fired—I was quite positive about that. Might he have fallen from a tree, and be lying in pain somewhere, his leg broken, not daring to risk a shout for help? I was inclined to favour this latter view, perhaps because we had grown so cocky that we felt our expertise and experience put us beyond the point of being foolish enough to commit the sort of blunder that would lead to discovery by a patrol or by any aboriginal. Or it could have been, I suppose, that my subconscious instinct was to react with terror and horror to the possibility of being separated from Minakawa, and that, as a result, I was suppressing any acceptance of such a possibility.

Not one leaf rustled from dark to dawn without my being aware of it, that night—and the next morning I was up and off well before first light. I began a systematic search, leaving not a single yard unscrutinised, over an area of about half a square mile around the tree trunk where I had discovered Minakawa's rucksack and sandals the previous afternoon.

I left off and made my way back to the shelter two or three times, just in case Minakawa might have managed to get back there during my absence. But there was no sign of him and all I got in return for this to-ing and fro-ing was a growing feeling of despair at the futility of it all.

I spent the whole day until sunset grubbing around the area, without a hint of what might have happened to him. However, one thing I did conclude—that he had *not* been shot at and killed—from the fact that I'd not been able to discover traces of a single drop of blood. But this did not help a great deal—because it led to the fear that if Minakawa had not been killed by aboriginals, then the alternative was that he'd been captured by the Americans ...

And then, in my mind, a whole host of the implications that the word "prisoner" has for a Japanese; and the final memory of what that officer had said: *"They always kill all their prisoners."*

So now I was the only one left. I was on my own: and I knew I could not survive on my own. I realised I should have to move away from this point near the coast, further towards the interior of the island. With a heavy heart, I began in a lack-lustre way to stuff some of my possessions into a rucksack. There seemed no point in prolonging the search any further: Minakawa, my friend, was gone.

Abruptly, my reverie was interrupted by a peculiar chattering drone from above the treetops. It seemed to be coming nearer, too. A prey to nameless fears, I sprang out from under the tarpaulin roof of the shelter and peered up into the sky.

Between the branches of the huge trees, I saw the outline of a helicopter!

I looked again and saw that there were in fact two helicopters. I was too startled to think of fleeing or taking cover and I stood, staring dumbly up at those machines, rooted to the spot like a rabbit fascinated by a snake. Suddenly the aircraft began to lose height; one seemed as though it was going to drop down and land right on top of me! It was so low that I could make out the features of the men inside it (and I could see, thanks to my jungle-sharpened eyesight, that they were taking photographs, too).

The helicopters now began taking it in turns to skim the very tops of the trees above the shelter—and at last I panicked. I grabbed my rucksack, ripped off the tarpaulin, and made off as fast as ever I could into the scrub; the thickest scrub, where I couldn't be picked out, examined like a butterfly on a pin, from the sky....

My brain was bursting with confused thoughts. I'd never been convinced that a man could live on alone in the jungle —the jungle itself would not allow it. Nevertheless, there

146

must have been some faint, subconscious hope deep down inside me that *my* case *might* be different. Now even this hope was denied me: I shouldn't even be permitted to put it to the test, for they would seek me out and kill me first; I was at the mercy of our enemies, after all this time.

It was too late now to get away—they knew where I was; they had seen me from the sky. It was too late to move camp—their machines could scout in a few minutes an area it would take me days to cross. It was too late to hide any more—with their resources, now they knew I was there to look for, they'd have me within hours....

Very well then: if it had to be, it had to be. I would stop running and turn to face them. But if I had to die, then I was going to make sure it was a glorious death!

First, I would bury all the tools and all the things that had helped me keep going in the jungle for so long—I'd bury them in the ground by the roots of a scrub bush. And I went to the secret cave where all my valuables were stored away, all the precious things I'd thought of as fated to die with me, and I buried them too. No American executioners were going to get their hands on *those*....

Just as I was starting to spread the "grave" with dry leaves, I remembered my diary, tucked safely away between two rocks inside the cave. But there was no time to go back for it now, so it had to stay where it was. What a pity! It had now gone to four volumes—all written on note-books salvaged from the American tip. The last entry must remain as May 16th, 1960 (I learned later that this should really have been May 22nd: we had lost six days somewhere in those sixteen years!).

I set off climbing, finally, mounting towards "Triangle Heights"—the high plateau behind us where the American army flag always flew. I wonder why it was that I chose to climb these particular slopes ... the hill with the American camp at its summit? Perhaps, having decided that I could escape no more and that all that remained was to meet the enemy and be slaughtered, I had decided that I'd like the place of my death to be an open and rocky one. If so, the area of the camp was a fair enough choice.

I made my way up the slope through the scrub, which became sparser and sparser until I was labouring across a stretch of almost bare rock. As I clambered over the weathered and fissured stone, I happened to lift my head and gaze upwards towards the brow of the hill.

Not far away, four Americans stood looking down at me.

I'd been carrying a square of old trouser material. I lifted it over my head and waved it. Now that the moment of truth had come; now that I was finally face to face, after sixteen years, with the enemy we had always dreaded, curiously I felt no panic, no fear. I watched almost dispassionately as one of the quartet detached himself and advanced down the slope towards me. I'd no time to wonder if he was going to kill me then and there—for an instant later I was engulfed, swamped, overwhelmed by a shock and a surprise as heart-stopping as anything I'd experienced in my whole life.

The face of the "American" approaching me was that of a tidily-shaven, neatly hair-cut, gentle-eyed Minakawa!

The smile with which he greeted me was indescribable. I'd not seen an expression on his face like it for years and years. I stared at him unbelievingly: he had been fitted out in smart Western-style civilian clothes and wore brand-new shoes on his feet. "That was a bit of luck, finding you here just like that, wasn't it?" he asked as nonchalantly as ever.

I couldn't find a word to say. All I could do was whisper his name over and over again. My thoughts of dying a valiant death had vanished into thin air.

Now the three Americans, who had tactfully remained at a distance during our meeting, were approaching. With all that remained of the soldier in me coming unconsciously out, I drew myself up smartly and faced them at attention.

"You're all right now, are you?" one of them asked gently, looking at me curiously but not unkindly.

He was a military policeman. One of his colleagues was also an M.P., and the third man was an interpreter. I was surprised to find he spoke Japanese better than we did (and I learned later that he was a *nisei*, an American-born Japanese, by the name of Robert Tsutsui).

"I was in that helicopter, you know! Could you see me? We thought we saw you," Minakawa was saying excitedly. "We've already been to the shelter on foot today—but it looked as though you'd made off to hide somewhere else.... I was getting worried.... I never dreamed we'd chance together here like this!"

I was taken with Minakawa to a small truck standing on a road nearby. I was dying to ask him what had happened— but as I got in I was wrestling more with the sombre thought: "They always kill their prisoners." I still firmly believed it and I wondered if he did.

The truck turned on to the main road leading through the jungle and drove quickly towards the north-east. The trees and the scrub sped past, now receding from the verges, now almost meeting overhead. "I don't suppose I shall ever have the chance of seeing this jungle again," I mused, and turned my head towards Minakawa, intending to put the thought into words. But his face was turned away from me as he gazed quietly back along the highway at the green wilderness now disappearing behind us for ever. So I kept quiet and silently turned round myself to watch as the jungle sank from view.

This was a special goodbye; goodbye to the springtime of our youth, squeezed out of us and soaked up by that jungle; goodbye to sixteen lost years, lost and buried for ever in the depths of the forest—sixteen years that could never be given back to us.

III

SKY, BASE AND HOME

1

Agana Naval Hospital

During the truck journey, Minakawa told me what had happened to him.

After we had parted company that day, he had carried on trying to track down the chicken for a while. But he could find no sign of it and, as he stopped for a breather, he took a look round and suddenly realised that he'd got as far as the grove near the road leading to the coastal highway.

He was fed up with the fruitless search for the chicken, so he changed plans and thought he'd have a try for some breadfruit. However, once he'd transferred his attention from the ground to the trees, he noticed a coconut palm only five or six yards away where the nuts looked to be at least on the way to ripening. Changing plans once more, he decided to try for these.

He put his rucksack down, slipped off his sandals and shinned up the coconut palm. He'd managed to knock down half a dozen, when he heard voices coming from a cluster of rocks over to his left. He swung himself round to look. A couple of aboriginals, jabbering away to each other at the tops of their voices, were making their way towards him. He slithered down the palm as fast as he could and, with no time to slip his feet into his sandals, made off in the opposite direction, jettisoning his rucksack where he'd put it down.

But poor Minakawa, in his run-down condition, had

managed barely a hundred yards before he felt a terrible throbbing behind his left ear. He began to go dizzy and his head swam so violently that he found difficulty in staying on his feet. He battled on for a further hundred yards or so, and then ran slap into the arms of the aboriginals! They had evidently managed to outflank him, and made short work of overpowering him.

They were young men, far fitter than he, and lost no time in binding his hands behind his back. There followed some rough handling in the course of which he gathered they wanted him to get moving. Minakawa realised there was no point in resistance, so, abandoning all attempts at giving them a run for their money, he fell in line and set off walking in the direction they indicated. Their route turned out to be a slantwise path through the jungle, which brought them out eventually to the road that follows the line of the coast. At this point he was ordered to halt.

The two aboriginals seemed as if they were waiting for a truck or something to pass, for they looked regularly and eagerly up and down the road. And there was a fair amount of traffic—but, the moment the drivers caught a sight of Minakawa, they threw up their hands in horror, indicated that they couldn't pick him up, and drove on! The aboriginals seemed to realise that there was no future in this, so, after another bit of rough handling and prodding, they bundled him off again, this time to a nearby office which looked like a branch police post. The locals got wind of the event in no time at all, and came crowding round in a chattering throng.

Poor Minakawa nearly gave up the ghost at this point, quite resigned to its being the beginning of the end. However, in no time at all, he was put into a truck and taken right across the island, from the east coast to the west, and deposited at a large hospital. This was the American Naval Hospital at Agana.

"They took me inside and, before anything else, I was shoved into a lovely, piping hot bath. Then, when I was

through, they cut my hair for me—didn't they make a fine
job of it? And they gave me these clothes. Then they started
talking to me and asking questions. 'You weren't all on
your own, were you?' ... 'There's a whole group of you
back there in the jungle, isn't there?' ... and so on. At first I
stuck out that I was the only one; that there weren't any
others: but they got more and more searching and insistent
and, anyhow, they realised that a man can't live through on
his own out there. So, in the end, I was forced into con-
fessing about you. They said they'd get a search going for
you, and told me I was to act as guide.

"The idea seemed to be set out for you at once but, in the
end, and after a lot of to-ing and fro-ing, it turned out that
we couldn't get off before today. When it came to the off
and they told me we'd be coming for you in a *helicopter*,
you could have knocked me down with a feather! I mean,
after all, we're nothing more than ordinary Japanese
soldiers; it didn't seem on the cards that they'd put one of us
in a helicopter just to look for the other!"

A large, beautiful building came into view. "There's the
hospital." Minakawa said this in his normal voice; then,
putting his lips close to my ear, he added in a whisper, "It
looks as if they're planning on getting us back to Japan in
no time at all."

There was a whole world of distrust and misgiving in the
look I gave him! "You'd better watch it, boy!" I told myself seriously.

At the hospital, Minakawa's ways and mine parted yet
again. A young-looking American motioned me to follow
him and I was led away and shown into a neat and tidy
room. I was stripped of my tattered and really splendidly
patched rags. Then I was led to the showers, where some
soap and a towel were placed ready for me.

Standing under the lovely stream of hot water in that
shower, rubbing in the soap and feeling myself gradually
come clean—a bath had never felt like this before, in my
whole life! I'd had the odd cold splash in a jungle stream

155

during those sixteen years—but it was a very risky thing to do and, as far as I can remember, I hadn't dared indulge more than two or three times at the most. So it wasn't just dirt on my body—it was a solid layer of filth, caked so hard that it acted almost as a second skin. As I stood under that shower, it literally peeled off me as if a whole skin was coming away!

We had allowed our hair to grow as it pleased. It was about two feet long, and we used to bind it up in a topknot with a piece of home-made thong to stop it from drooping down untidily and getting in our way. As I washed my hair, I realised that I would soon lose it and have it shorn off like Minakawa—and the thought made me strangely and surprisingly sad, as if I knew in advance I was going to be separated from a long-established friend.

After I had managed to get rid of the best part of all the caked filth by dint of a lot of scrubbing, I went out through the screen of the shower cubicle and the young American who had been waiting for me, grinning all over his face, handed me a shirt and some long trousers which looked as if they might be naval uniform. The old tatters that I'd taken off were tidied away and put by somewhere.

I put on the shirt and stepped into a pair of underpants and the trousers. Then I was handed a pair of pyjamas which had the delightfully fresh smell of something newly laundered. They seemed far too large for me, but when I tried slipping an arm into the sleeve, I found that they fitted as well as I could have expected even if they'd been tailored for me.

I was taken out of the room, put into an elevator which deposited me on the fourth floor, taken down a long corridor and shown into a room full of all sorts of medical equipment and apparatus. Here, a blue-eyed army doctor gave my whole body a searching examination and, it seemed, was unable to find anything radically wrong.

After this physical check-up, I was led to the barber-shop and a start was made on cutting my topknot—the hair that had known neither the sound nor the feel of scissors for sixteen years. I was quite surprised to find how the feeling of heaviness which I'd suffered from for so long suddenly vanished! And I was fascinated by the long-forgotten snip-snipping noise. . . .

Next, they had a go at my beard and whiskers, which were all of an inch long and very grubby and unkempt. That was a wonderful feeling, too, as they spread the lather and the razor glided over my cheeks, my chin and my upper lip!

Then a camera was produced and a whole range of photographs was taken, from every conceivable angle, almost as though I was some weird and wonderful animal.

While all this was going on, my thoughts kept straying back to my dear old topknot, lying lifeless and rejected on a table. If the end was to come and was not far off, it would solace me to have my topknot with me—for I looked on it as very much an intimate part of myself. All the same, I felt, they were certainly going to a lot of trouble if we were merely to be put against a wall and shot. Perhaps some more recondite fate was in store for us. . . .

When they'd done, therefore, I signalled that I'd like to keep the topknot. The barber didn't appear in the least taken aback, and with an "Ah!" which I could have sworn was more sympathy than surprise he reached for it and cheerfully handed it over.

Then it was time to eat. God, that food tasted marvellous; really marvellous! There was a pile of bread on a plate—bread whiter than I'd ever imagined bread could be; quite bewildered, I couldn't take my eyes off it. They brought us soup, steak, and course after course of dishes I'd never eaten before and which I can't tell you the names of. As each new plateful was served to us (Minakawa had been brought in and sat down by my side at the same table), we found we just couldn't help looking round the ring of beaming American faces surrounding us. I was still sure it was part of a plot, though.

When at length we'd finished eating, we went back to the room that had been set aside for us. It looked like a ward but there were only two beds in it, so now at last there was an opportunity for the two of us to talk without being overheard.

"I still don't believe it."

"I don't either; I *can't* believe it."

"They can treat us as generously and as warmly as they like, but here's one they won't be taking in," I said in the undertone that was now ingrained habit for me.

"You're right. No, we've got to keep our eyes wide open all the time. We'd better help each other, so we don't let up for a second. When all's said and done, after all, we're prisoners; there's no two ways about that."

We still spoke under our breath, still used the same shifty glance around us that had become almost second nature while we were hiding away in the jungle.

During the afternoon we were brought out of our room again and taken in the elevator to the ground floor. Here we were led into a huge room where a horde of newspaper reporters, cameras cocked at the ready, were waiting eagerly for us. Minakawa and I were sat down facing a big table. There followed a flood of words—not a single one of which we understood—from the foreign reporters' lips. There was a row of several dozen long, thin, tube-like things ranged in front of us.

We had agreed earlier not to blab anything out thoughtlessly, so even to the questions in perfect Japanese which flowed insidiously from the interpreter's mouth, we did not give anything in the way of detail in our replies.

We were asked first where our homes were in Japan, and questions then followed about date of birth, families, army career and so on.

The next group of questions was about the sort of life we had led during the sixteen years since we had landed on Guam. We answered in turn, picking our way backwards through a long list of memories, and we tried our best to be

158

accurate. And after I'd finished my part of the story, I added this final remark: "If it hadn't been for Minakawa falling into your hands, it would probably have worked out that we would have spent the rest of our time, till our dying day, in the jungle."

"Are there still other Japanese soldiers like you left in the jungle?"

"We don't know. Probably not. After we'd lost Umino, we ourselves never set eyes on any."

"Did you know that Japan was defeated in the war?"

"No. The idea had occurred to us as a possibility—but we could never really bring ourselves to believe in our country's defeat."

This was how we felt about it and we said so, quite openly and honestly.

On the following day, we were again summoned to the medical room and we acted as the interpreter directed. The examination that followed was much more thorough and detailed than on the previous day. They took a whole series of X-rays, recorded our finger-prints and even made records of the cast of our footprints!

For the last test, they put a syringe needle into us, in a vein in each arm, and took some blood from us. They filled the whole of the syringe, the blood gleaming black through the glass. I felt almost as if I might throw a faint while this was going on—and I was reassured to learn afterwards that Minakawa had reacted in something of the same way.

We got back to the room we'd been given, dropped on the beds and stretched out full length, and then began to talk.

"I still think they could be meaning to kill us, after all. I've never in all my life had as much blood as that taken from me; and all in one go too! Yes—taking our blood from us bit by bit and letting us die a slow death—that could well be what their little game is!"

"Do you think they meant any of it when they promised they'd be sending us back to Japan straightaway?"

"I wish I knew. Maybe they were just making fools of us. We were always told they killed their prisoners, weren't we?"

"Well if they're making fools of us and it gets to the point of us tossing our lives away, I think we'd do far better if we tried to make a dash for it—now!"

"Yes. You're right. Let's have a go at getting out from under ... before they get a chance to take any more blood from us."

Feeling pretty weak and wobbly, we crept towards the door. But the key was turned; we weren't to be allowed to get as far as the corridor.

"This means we were right! We're *not* going to be returned to Japan. We'll be shut up in this room and then, when they're ready, they'll kill us. We're prisoners all right!"

"Let's jump from the window and make a run for it, shall we?" Then we realised that our room was on the fourth floor, and that it would be quite impossible to jump from that height. . . .

We found that we simply couldn't get rid of this idea that, if we were taken prisoner, we should be killed by our captors. It had been encrusted in our minds, we had lived by it for so long that it wasn't to be eradicated on the instant. It had been dinned into our heads eighteen years previously and we'd not been allowed to forget it; now we *couldn't* forget it!

My whole body felt listless and heavy almost beyond bearing; it was just as though I'd got a terrible fever coming on.

Minakawa suddenly jerked himself upright on the bed. "I'm going to stick my head in a noose and end it all that way. I cannot stick this uncertainty." He was standing on the bed now.

I heaved myself to my feet and stood beneath him. For the gentle Minakawa, who always played everything so cool, to get so het up was unprecedented. "Go on then! Stick it

160

in a noose!"—I thought it best to be jeering rather than sympathetic—"Stick it in a noose and see how much good it does you! But remember it takes more than a few seconds to snuff it that way; they'll discover you in no time and have you down before you've had half a chance to finish the job...."

To my great relief, this worked—probably because, like me, Minakawa believed at the time that we were under constant and secret surveillance even when we appeared to be alone in our room! At any rate, he dropped back on to his bed and stretched out at full length again with his face to the wall.

2

Half Believing, Half Doubting

The interpreter came to see us quite regularly, always with the same story: "Very soon now, you'll be allowed to go back to Japan. Very soon you'll be with your families again." We almost wanted to say it for him!

He always smiled as he spoke. But, deep down, we found we just couldn't bring ourselves to believe him; we were convinced it was just another little trick, all part of the Big Trap! After all, you cannot switch your whole outlook as readily as you change a suit of clothes: the caution which had become second nature with us was not to be ignored all that easily. And each of us kept encouraging the other not to relax it for a second....

Two or three days after this, Minakawa set off early in the morning accompanied by a party of American soldiers. He was to lead them to the site of the old shelter where we'd been living when Umino died, from which they were to recover his mortal remains. I wasn't feeling at all well, still unable to shake off the fever that threatened, so I stayed behind. But I was on tenterhooks until they returned.

The expedition, for one thing, seemed in a way to put things in a fresh light: perhaps all their talk was *not* just a pack of lies, if they really were going to the trouble of finding Umino's remains for us to take back to Japan with us! Even so, it was still too soon for us to put complete confidence in them (we had decided before Minakawa left), and we must each keep very much on the alert still.

It was afternoon before Minakawa returned to the hospital. All that was left of Umino was stowed in a sealed box.

"There was only the skull that was still in good order, I'm afraid," Minakawa said. "The rest had all disintegrated pretty badly...." Like the good Buddhist he was, his soft voice and gentle eyes became filled with compassion as he related how they had dug where we had buried Umino's body.

"Still," he concluded, "it could have been a good deal worse. On the way there, I couldn't stop myself imagining that he might have been dug up and eaten by a dog or something awful like that...."

Quite soon after this, we were told that a newspaperman had shown up from Japan and we were taken to meet him. The moment he saw us, he whipped out his name cards and gave one to each of us. This hark-back to good old Japanese practice took us so much by surprise that we were quite dumbstruck for a moment or two. Then, I found myself instinctively reverting to the army habits of sixteen years previously and gave him a deep bow. When we finally got round to words, he told us that he had been asked to come out to us by our families, and he showed us letters from home.

Still half in doubt, and yet half wanting to believe it all, I picked one of them up and looked at it. It was signed by my younger sister. And there was another, separate letter from mother. My father had died three years before.

While I was still reading, the newspaperman began asking questions.

162

"So, after sixteen long years, you're finally all set for going back to Japan. Don't you find it just that little bit frightening?"

"No, of course not. There's nothing frightening about it," Minakawa replied, his manner a little short.

"What sort of a life did you lead during those sixteen years?"

"We kept count of the date by watching the moon. Itō here kept a diary pretty nearly all the time. We ate all sorts of things, just about anything we could manage to lay hands on—berries, grass roots, the lot. We lived in caves and in shelters we built for ourselves in the jungle. For myself, the harder it got, the more intolerable it became, the more I put my faith in the Spirits and the Buddha to see me through."

"What sort of life do you plan to lead after you're back in Japan?"

"For myself, having seen so many of my friends die in the fighting or in the jungle afterwards, and having been granted to come through it alive and get back to Japan unscathed, I'm planning on entering the Buddhist priesthood."

"And you, Itō?"

"I shall rest up for a while and get myself really well again before I make any plans."

"These are dried grapes from Kōfu. Would you like them?" The reporter brought out a little package for us as he said this.

My hand trembled violently as I reached forward to take the parcel. I looked at it for what seemed an age—but somehow I just couldn't bring myself to unwrap it. There was still that awful feeling of suspicion and disquiet; it kept coming back into my mind time and time again and I could find no way of ridding myself of it. I even suspected the authenticity of my sister's signature.

Then, as had happened a few days before, we were surrounded by a horde of newspapermen. This time there

163

were both the local people and reporters covering our story for papers across the world.

They told us that arrangements had been made for our families to talk to us on the international line from Tokyo. I caught Minakawa's eye and managed to get a signal to him that I knew only he would understand. We both of us were still quite convinced that it was all part of a great big trap. I was completely fogged by now. I just didn't know if I'd be able to tell whether it was my family or not on the line.

All sorts of people had crowded into the room where the telephone conversation was to take place. In one corner was an instrument they told us was a television set (I'd never seen one before, of course). There was a voice coming out of it, with words that I just couldn't get the sense of.

We were so on edge, and there was so much noise, that I found I couldn't be sure whether the voice I heard coming from the telephone receiver was really my younger sister's or not. So, as Minakawa and I had agreed beforehand, I simply replied in monosyllables.

"It's me—*Kimiko*! Don't you know who I am?"

"Of course I know."

"They say you're not all that well. Is it true? *How* are you?"

"I'm quite all right; there's nothing the matter with me."

"We're dying to see you; we're planning a wonderful feast."

"M'hmm."

"Oh, it'll be just like it always used to be. . . ."

"We'll see. I must go now. I'm afraid I must go. . . ."

More confused than ever, I passed the receiver to Minakawa. I could hear from his voice that he was as suspicious as I was. "Yes . . . Yes, this is Minakawa . . . Is that my elder sister Tsuru? . . . Can you tell me how many acres of land we have at the back of the house? . . . That's right . . . Can you remind me of my grandfather's given-name? . . . Good . . . No, I'm afraid I don't know. I'm sorry that must be all for now."

164

He took the receiver from his ear and looked hard at it—as though he was trying to establish whether the words it had brought to him had been true or false!

When we got back to our room and discussed it all, we still couldn't make up our minds. We went over the telephone conversations again and again—and also the visit of the Japanese newspaperman. Yet while we were casting the most severe doubts on the authenticity of those we had spoken to on the telephone, in the next breath we were trying to decide what to take them home as presents! It was very odd.

Finally we decided to preserve open minds on the whole thing—but to relax our caution not a jot. "Even if it really was them talking to us on the phone, you see," Minakawa said gravely, "there might have been someone standing over them and forcing them to say what they did, mightn't there? ... No—we can't put complete trust in the thing until our feet actually find themselves on Japanese soil again."

If there'd been half the chance of getting away, I think we'd probably have seized it with open arms and worked out some sort of plan of escape, right there and then!

3

Preparations for the Return

Very early the following morning, the interpreter came to our room. In his usual attractive voice, which I found tended to put you off your guard, he asked us first of all how we were feeling. (We'd decided that this attractiveness in his voice was a natural part of his manner and that therefore there was nothing particularly sinister in it.) Then he added: "There's been a rather sudden change in the plans for your return to Japan."

We managed to exchange glances without his noticing. Though not a word or sound had passed between us, these glances were the means of conveying our old jungle warning sign. We were both now ready for anything, on our guard. "Let me tell you why we've done this. It's because we understand everybody back in your home towns has made all kinds of preparations—and they're so much on tenterhooks that they just can't bear to hang on a day more than is absolutely necessary. So, we've decided to advance the schedule; and the plan now is that you're to be sent home to Japan on the 10.05 plane this morning."

Almost as he finished speaking, a couple of nurses came into the room, each with a pile of things provided for us by the American service people. There were brand new underclothes, shirts, civilian suits, shoes, ties and everything we would need for the journey.

Minakawa and I exchanged glances yet once more— we'd better resign ourselves to it all, these glances meant. And we began changing into these new clothes and stripping off the Aloha shirts we'd been made to wear up till now.

Minakawa's suit was a dark brown, mine a lighter colour. I managed, under my own steam, to get all my new clothes on; but when it got to the tie, I began to run into trouble. It really was just that bit too much for me, in the state I was in, trying to make a knot! They were lovely ties—Minakawa's was a purple colour, and mine had a sort of crystal pattern on it. So the nurse stood close in front of me and tied it defly for me. She was a foreign woman, I know, and that was the thought that was uppermost. Yet even so she was a woman, the first one I'd got near for more than sixteen years, and there was something about the smell of her that got me all worked up and excited. And, of course, remember my sense of smell was very acute after all my jungle experience.

The nurses gave us a slight bow as they left the room and, the minute we were left alone, we both of us at almost

166

exactly the same time began to move towards each other. Minakawa was the first to speak.

"He said they were returning us to Japan. But I still don't put any faith in it. I still can't really believe it whole-heartedly."

"No... I can't believe it either. What they'll do, I bet, is get us on that plane and then take us off somewhere else. Or, if it's not that, it'll be a case of shoving us out of the plane somewhere on the way. That's it—they're going to kill us by shoving us out of the plane!"

"Well, if that's it, that's it: there's nothing more we can do."

Minakawa sounded extremely calm and collected. I really did take my hat off to him in this situation. I realised that I'd better try and calm down myself and take it easy.

I used one of the bags we'd been given to wrap up the topknot that had adorned my head until only a few days ago. Yes—we were right ... We were going to be flung out of the plane over the middle of the Pacific. This was the fate of the prisoner, I reflected....

4

Take off, Landing

Just as we were leaving the American Naval Hospital at Agana, we were each given a really rather smart wrist watch as a farewell present.

My watch said half-past-nine as we were put in a car which took us to Agana airport. Presently, we were led to an aeroplane—along with Umino's remains. It was a large, four-engined plane. Tsutsui, the interpreter, was with us. But we were the only two Japanese. This kept our suspicions alive and strong as ever—we still couldn't shake ourselves free from the idea that we were on the way to our graves, even now!

On time, at 10.05, we took off from Guam—the island that had robbed us of our youth; Guam that had been such a joyless, thankless place for us.

We watched the wide expanse of ocean below us. And, as time passed, I began to feel the murky forebodings that had clouded my mind gradually clear a little. "We should be catching sight of Japan pretty soon now," the interpreter told us.

Suddenly, my eyes filled with tears. I just couldn't stop the flow. I stuck my forehead as close as it would go to the window and let them stream down my cheeks unchecked. I knew well enough that Minakawa had his eye on me—but I guessed that he couldn't have been very far from tears himself. The Pacific was so far below us that the waves seemed to have gone still, to be stamped on the ocean as far as you could see, like the wrinkles on a sheet of used paper.

At last, I lifted my gaze from the sea, quietly closed my eyes, and wiped away my tears. "There's nothing to be ashamed of in dropping a few tears at a time like this," I told myself. "It's beginning to look as though we were wrong after all," I thought. I was still looking out of the port-hole. Cloud was streaming past now, gradually increasing. "I wonder where it *was* that we went wrong? No, no, no: the mistake started right at the very beginning, with the very first day of the sixteen years that sapped all our youth and vitality...."

"Itō! ... Itō ..."

I was jolted out of my day-dreaming by Minakawa. He had been shouting at the top of his voice, but I was too late to catch the sense of what he was saying.

Now I'd been brought back to my senses, I looked out again; but the cloud had thickened even more and there was now nothing at all to be seen. The interpreter told us that we must be over Japan by now.

168

Our native land was to be hidden from us that little bit longer!

I felt the plane making a huge arc—as if to sport with my sense of frustration. And I suddenly sensed that underneath us it wasn't Japan, but a frightening country that I didn't know.

However, the doubts and the suspicions were all gone— the doubts that had made me fear that all there was in store for me was death. Or so I thought—but they were only too easily re-aroused. "He's waiting for the mist to clear," explained the interpreter. And as he said this, I was assailed by a new doubt greater than any of the others. I couldn't stop myself from shouting, "Supposing Japan's a part of enemy territory, like Guam? Whatever would happen to us then?"

Just then, I felt the engines throttle back. I became all tense, and suddenly realised how excited I was.

Land came into sight, and buildings. As we touched down on the runway, an unpleasant sense of foreboding began to steal over me. We were landing at Tachikawa Air Base.

"We're coming in to land, we're coming in to land." I kept repeating the words to myself, trying to snap out of the succession of unreasonable and numbing fears and give myself the guts to stand up and move to the steps that had been brought alongside the plane's exit hatch. It looked as though Minakawa, too, was having exactly the same sort of problem.

"We're here! We're here, safe and sound. We're really back home at last!" I kept saying it over and over, in an effort to force back the tears that were threatening to well up again.

"Well, we made it, didn't we?" said Minakawa. There was hardly a trace of emotion in his voice.

There was now nobody left in the airplane seats. They'd all got up and were making their way out of the plane and down the gangway. Minakawa stood up and began to walk slowly towards the exit door. He went through the hatch and started to go slowly down the steps. I followed, a couple of paces behind him.

"*Banzai! Banzai!*"

For the moment, I couldn't for the life of me believe that the huge crowd jostling in front of me had gathered especially to welcome us back to Japan.

At the head of the crowd, a banner fluttered bravely in the fresh breeze. I saw that my name was written on the banner—and, as I think back to it, I always wonder what sort of an expression there was on my face at that moment.

I didn't know whether to laugh or cry. The crowds started to surge towards us as we came down the gangway. For a moment, I faltered and almost stopped. But Minakawa carried on in front of me, and, without so much as a wave to the crowds, solemnly and deliberately planted his feet on the ground. I followed on behind, and took my first step on the Motherland.

In a flash, Minakawa and I were completely surrounded by the welcoming crowd. I caught a glimpse of my mother's face, but I'd no sooner seen it than it became lost again among the bobbing sea of smiles, as everybody jostled round us. At last I had managed to force my way through to where she was and had got my arms about her shoulders. Then I was hugging my sister, who was by her side.

It all seemed part of a marvellous dream. I wasn't going to allow myself to be parted from mother and my sister any more, and I got an arm firmly clasped round each of them. I don't remember a word of what I said to them.

After what seemed an age, we were led to a room on the first floor of a building that stood just by the side of the runway. There, we were put through the immigration formalities. "Everything is in order, then, is it?" asked the immigration control man. He seemed to be checking my bona fides with my mother and sister. "As if, today of all days, any bloody thing *could* be out of order," I thought; I had a hard job to stop the words coming out pat!

After this, we found ourselves being hemmed in by the crowd once more as we were led to a spacious reception room. Right at the head of the room, there was a large table, stacked with a jumble of several dozen microphones. We were led to chairs placed at the centre of the table and made to go through yet one more press conference. I was sitting next to Minakawa. My mother and sister and Minakawa's elder sisters came to sit on each side of us.

The press conference was an exact replica of the one we'd already been through in Guam. There was a battery of television cameras pointing at our faces. We had lived so long in the dim light of the jungle that the glare of the lamps dazzled us and made us screw up our eyes. In front of us, on the other side of the table, as many as a hundred newspapermen were pushing their way into the room.

I could feel myself breaking out in a sweat. I wasn't at all easy about all these press conferences; but, even so, I was a good deal happier than when we'd been made to attend that first one.

For one thing, I was home in Japan; there I was, with no possible doubt about it, safely back, my mother and my sister at my side. Again, at the earlier conference in Guam, I was still mistaken about the real intentions of the people questioning me, and I still felt the shadow of death looming and hovering in front of me. On the other hand, there was a disadvantage to balance these facts: in Guam, we'd had the interpreter between us and the reporters, and he'd conveyed both questions and replies to the other side. This had given us a regular respite and had lightened the ordeal somewhat. Now, it was different; even though only one man questioned us at a time, his questions came straight at us, with no one to intercept.

There wasn't all that much difference between the questions now and those we'd been asked in Guam. "How do you feel now you're back in Japan?"—This was easily the most difficult of all to answer. What could I have said— other than that I felt as if my heart was full to the brim? I

171

thought this was the best thing to say—it was true, at least —so I said it.

After this reply, I looked round at my mother's and my sister's faces; then my eyes met Minakawa's. There was a joy in his eyes that he couldn't conceal, and that I'd never seen before. Here we were, together still, and sitting next to the people we'd told each other about thousands of times back in the jungle!

"What was it that made you come out of the jungle?"

"Well, we'd completely run out of food: so I set out to try to find some tree berries or fruit..." Minakawa embarked yet again on the story of his capture.

Then it was my turn to describe once more how I felt when I realised he wasn't coming back. I got to the part where I found his abandoned rucksack and sandals—and there I stopped.

I found I just couldn't go any further with the story. It felt as if my emotions were rampaging right through me. I wanted to stick my arms round Minakawa, pull him close to me, and blubber all over him.

At last I felt I could carry on.

"The only reason I'd been able to survive for sixteen years in a place like that was this friend here. If I wasn't able to find him, I'd decided that the only thing for it was to kill myself."

"What were they like, all those deaths died so nobly by our Japanese soldiers?"

This new line of questioning was beginning to leave a pretty sour taste in my mouth.

"It's not the sort of subject you can deal with in just an hour or two," I said curtly, gritting my teeth in my growing impatience.

"Tell us about Umino at the time of his death."

I'd been looking at the ceiling. I lowered my gaze to the people in front of me, and the distaste of it all hit me once again. While I was taking time to settle myself before I dare reply, I heard Minakawa's voice, cool and collected as ever:

172

"His whole body was wasting away. He couldn't get any-where near sufficient to eat. The end came for him because he had too little food—and what little he did get was coarse and rough and involved too much hard labour. All this ex-hausted him and sapped every bit of energy he had. To have a companion die on you like this is pretty much the same as to die yourself, you know. You can't have any idea what a trial it was, how hard it was for us to live through it all...."

I was absolutely fed up with it all by now. I didn't want to have to speak another word. I felt a dull weight in my head, as if someone had dumped a load of lead there. All I wanted was to be able to escape from all these people, and get home to be with my family. It couldn't happen quickly enough.

But the questions carried on.

Minakawa was speaking again. "Yes, we saw the leaflets all right. But we were convinced that they were spurious and were meant as a trap. None of us believed they were genuine...."

"What was the hardest thing of all about the jungle...?"

"When did you realise the war was over...?"

"What did you do when there was nothing to eat...?"

"How did it feel when you first saw Japan again?"

"We still couldn't be sure it *was* Japan. When the plane came in to land, we were watching the roads very closely: you see we were not by any means free of the suspicion that we were being taken to America. So we wanted to find out if the traffic was keeping to the right, American style. Then we saw some cars ... driving on the left ... and we heaved yet one more sigh of relief! This certainly meant that it wasn't America. So it was probably safe to assume it was Japan after all!"

"What do you plan to do with your lives, now you're home...?"

"Itō—there was a party that went to Guam—round about 1953, it was—to gather the remains of Japanese soldiers who died there. They reported finding a quantity of seals marked with your name. Did you make them in the hope that the news you were alive might percolate through?"

"Seal carving's a hobby of mine. When things were all calm and peaceful, I'd sit myself down in my shelter and busy myself with my carving. That was all it was—there was never the slightest intention of letting it be known I was still alive."

"Do you think there's anyone else like yourself still alive in Guam?"

I'd had enough. The same old questions—over and over again. It seemed they'd never bring it to an end. I didn't bother to reply. All I wanted was to be able to go home....

5

The Real Live Ghost

We'd got through all the formalities and, at last, they'd told us we were free to go. For the very first time ever, Minakawa and I faced each other without a care in the world.

"I suppose you're planning to get home straight away, as you're so near," said Minakawa. He still used the undertone that had become a habit with us.

"Yes. We're getting the 3.30 train at Hachiōji," I replied. "How about you?"

"We'll be spending the night in Tokyo. Then we'll get back home tomorrow."

"Where are you staying?"

"I don't know. My sister's got it all taken care of."

"Well ... This is goodbye then. Look after yourself, won't you?" I was so upset that I couldn't find any words better than this.

"You too, Itō. Take care of yourself ... and don't go tiring yourself out."

I nodded. We were back in Japan, in spite of everything. We didn't die in the jungle, after all.

We fixed on a day to meet up again. I suddenly realised that, from this moment on, we'd be living separate, independent lives—when, for the past sixteen years, all our actions had interlocked and made us almost into a single unit. There was a strange feeling, almost of loneliness, now we were to go our several ways.

We had a car to take us to Hachiōji station. I'd said goodbye to Minakawa, but somehow it felt as if he was in the car with me. I found it wasn't possible to think of it in any other way—there he was, sitting by my side, quiet, unobtrusive, composed as ever. There were the three of us—mother, sister and myself—sitting in a row in the back of the car; yet I found myself giving rein to the illusion that it might well have been Minakawa, not my mother, at my side.

"Oh, if only your father had managed to stay alive another three years...." Mother seemed to be trying to will him back to be with us in the back of that car.

They began telling me all about what had happened to the family during my long absence. My father had died in 1958, talking about me to the very end, apparently. My grandmother had gone earlier, in 1950. I was always her favourite and she never missed a chance of making a great fuss of me. "Your grandmother was eighty-seven when she passed on. And she never for one moment stopped believing that her favourite grandson was still alive and that he'd be home again sooner or later."

Apparently, for the whole of the five years from the end of the war until she died, my grandmother had got up every morning at 4.0 a.m. and had made what we call a "hundred-fold pilgrimage" to our parish shrine.

And my father had been just as steadfast in his conviction that I was still alive. To his dying day, he'd never believed the official communiqué announcing that I had been killed in action.

We got to Hachiōji and we'd just managed all to get seats when there was a surge of newspapermen pressing round me again. Their cameras flashed, their pencils and notepads were at the ready for another dose of news about Guam. It seemed as though this quest for interviews with me was never going to end.

My head had gone all fuzzy since we'd left Tachikawa and there were the beginnings of a real mother and father of a splitting headache. It felt for all the world as if we were being turned into a circus; it was as if mother, sister and I were doing some sort of performing act for the public. It was an intolerable situation, weighing heavily on me.

The cameramen were everywhere, shooting off at every single thing we did. Mother had only to lift her face and there'd be flash bulbs popping from all angles: my sister was eating an ice cream I'd bought for her, and every single mouthful was faithfully recorded on film. I bore it as well as I could; I'd placed mother in the window seat, and sat on the inside, choking back my anger for all I was worth.

Then we were off. But we still hadn't escaped from it all. Some of the damned newspapermen had decided to ride with us! I suddenly found myself thinking about the typhoons we'd lived through in Guam. We were gradually getting nearer to Yamanashi, and the old scenery I'd known since childhood was speeding by the carriage window.

Presently, we were at the point where the hills fall back at the edge of the Kōfu basin; I thought back to the day when I'd joined up in the East 63rds, and the memories of eighteen years ago came crowding into my mind as vividly as if it had all happened yesterday. As I let my eyes wander over the vineyards which stretched across the Kōfu basin as far as you could see, I began to feel a new joy, a fresh vitality inside me; it told me that here in this soil, the spring-time of my youth *was* still alive, vital as ever.

They were all watching me closely, trying to catch the

176

slightest feeling or reaction on my part. After a while, mother smiled at me; there was a whole load of memories and affection packed into that smile. It unleashed something in me too. I smiled back at her—completely relaxed now.

Then the newspapermen began poking questions at me again.

"What does it feel like to see the scenery of your birthplace once again? ... What do you feel about armies? ... Have you ever heard about the Cold War? ..."

The train pulled in to Kōfu station. There were crowds of people thronging the platform to meet me. Even before I got down on to the platform, they were shouting "Banzai", for all the world as if they were welcoming a victorious general back from a successful campaign!

The minute we'd stepped down, they'd encircled us completely. "My head's swimming worse than ever," I said; I suddenly realised I was still speaking in an undertone, though I knew well enough that Kōfu station platform wasn't the jungle!

Mother looked up at me. I returned her smile. Then I saw someone shoving his way desperately towards us through the crowds. I suddenly remembered the face. "Good Heavens! It's Kazumi!" I could not keep the shout back, I was so surprised.

I waved to him and waited as he forced his way towards us inch by inch. At long last we were near enough to grab each other's hands. "Hello! How wonderful."

There was a mist in front of my eyes now; all these reunions were getting a little too much for me.

We'd been close friends from our elementary school days; he was a bit older than I and I'd always tagged on to him as something like an elder brother.

Then the Governor of the County called for "Three Banzais". The whole station was jam-packed. Not a soul could move an inch.

I had to keep a happy smile on my face, as a thank-you to

them all for turning out to welcome me back. "There's well over a couple of thousand here, I'll bet," said Kazumi, sandwiching his words between the cheers.

We struggled to get through the crowd of well-wishers, making our way slowly towards the platform from which our branch-line trains started. When we got there, we found that this platform too was chock-a-block with people. They had stuck up a big banner here, too. It read, "Congratulations, Sergeant Itō! Long live patriotism like yours!" It was signed by an organisation which called itself the Society for the Protection of Japan.

The most surprising thing of all was that the same jostling throng and the same warm welcome met us at every single station along the line. It was as if the welcoming party somehow managed to get in front of us between stations, and lay out the whole reception ready for repetition when our train pulled in!

There were Women's Societies at every stop, their representatives stepping up to the side of the carriage and putting a bouquet in my hands as I stretched and reached forward from the window. I couldn't but put a smile on my face, accept the bouquets gracefully and thank them as warmly as I could. For one of these ladies could well have been one of the pretty young girls who had come to the trackside eighteen years before to wave me on my way when I'd joined my regiment!

It seemed an age before we got to our station. Here, too, it seemed as if everyone for miles around had turned out to meet us, and we were once more engulfed by the well-wishing crowds.

To cheer myself up, I kept telling myself that this was the end of it all, that I'd soon be able to relax behind the walls of our home. But I soon realised that I'd been a bit too hopeful! For all the village worthies had turned out too and were lining up on the platform to congratulate me on my safe return.

Oiso is the name of the little hamlet where I'd been born

and brought up: it lies about five miles from the station, on a road which leads back into the mountains. Apparently every single member of the hamlet had gone to the parish shrine and was waiting there to join me in a service to commemorate my safe home-coming. Dead tired, and with my heart brimming over with emotion at this unbelievable display by everyone, I was led to the parish shrine.

It was at this same shrine that there had been a service in honour of our joining our unit in January, eighteen years before. Those eighteen years had taken me first to Manchuria and then to Guam, and now I had come back to the point where it had all started. It was a journey I had no desire to repeat.

The congratulatory messages came to a close at last and, after I'd spoken a few short words of thanks, with my relatives forming a sort of guard of honour around me, we set off up the slope that led to the dear old house where I was born.

I went right through to the sitting-room in the innermost part of the house. They put me in the place of honour, with my back to the alcove. Behind me was a scroll painting and a flower arrangement. There was *sake* to mark the occasion; we passed the cups between us, draining them at a gulp and refilling them at once. And there were still more speeches commemorating my safe return home.

But I was now far too exhausted to take any of it in, much less to enjoy it and take any prominent part in it. All I wanted to do was to be allowed to stretch myself full length and sleep. I was eagerly anticipating my first fear-free night for sixteen years.

But it wasn't to be allowed me yet. My headache was still there, and it was getting worse. And I'd no need to feel my forehead to know that I'd got a fever or something; certainly I was running quite a temperature.

I wished to God they'd all leave me alone. I wanted, all on my own, to take a long look round the house, from top to bottom, round every single corner and cranny of it.

179

As it was, I'd to take a whole shipload of people with me wherever I went; all my old friends, every blessed relative, the newspapermen who'd tagged on since Tokyo—they came to see the silkworm rooms upstairs and the outhouse that father and I had built together back in 1940. Talking to them about memories of the old days passed the time well enough, but it didn't help to get me into a relaxed and easy mood.

Then, at last, they'd every one of them gone, and there was just the family left. They realised I didn't want any more talk and I gladly tucked myself up in the bed that my sister had made ready for me.

You're home; this is your home, I kept saying to myself as I shut my eyes. I was beautifully drowsy; but, just as I was dropping off, there was a faint noise that brought me wide awake again.

This isn't the jungle any more; there's no need to listen for any and every noise, I told myself. And I was just sinking into sleep again, when once more there was a noise and I was wide awake.

Whatever it was, there was to be no sleep for me that night. Somehow, everything inside me was out of gear.

The first thing my eyes rested on was the timber in the ceiling—was it that it wasn't the tarpaulin but ceiling timbers I saw? Or was it that, when I turned over in bed, there was no rustle from the grass and palm leaves of my jungle mattress? Or was it that my nerves just wouldn't take proper sleeping clothes, and a padded dressing gown—no matter how much I longed for them?

Whatever it was, I never got a wink of sleep.

It was raining. I could hear the drops spattering on the leaves. All I could think was that it was this noise that had stopped me from getting off to sleep. I got up and, still in my dressing gown, I went down from my bedroom to the hallway.

I could hear footsteps coming towards the house; there seemed to be quite a number of people. Instinctively, every nerve in my body went taut, as I turned myself to face the direction the sounds came from.

When they came into sight, it wasn't the villagers or my friends, but the crowd that had come with me from Tachikawa Base the previous day. The night before, there'd been all of fifty of them; but there weren't so many of them now —maybe thanks to the rain, I thought. I knew what their business was, by now. Asking questions, questions and more questions.

It was my sister who, the previous night, had mentioned that the village graveyard had a tombstone belonging to a real, live man. So, of course, we all had to go and see it.

We set off to climb the track up the hills behind the village. I led the way, the crowd of young Tokyo newsmen close on my heels. I found my wooden clogs hard to walk in: they were very different from our home-made jungle shoes. But I didn't bother to say anything about it—it would only have led to a whole new round of troublesome questions!

"What did you eat?"

"How did you sleep at night?"

"That time when the aboriginal shot at you—what did it feel like?"

"What did you do for clothes?"

They quizzed me about every little thing, these damned townees!

The sight of me standing in front of my own tombstone was really too good to be true for them. They all got their cameras trained and almost fought to get shots of me; and they kept on shooting, till I was heartily sick of it.

"*Itō Masashi, Section Leader in the Imperial Army of Japan . . .*" I read the inscription over and over again.

How could I describe my feelings? I stood there making a wry face, wishing all the people would go away. The fact that there were so many strangers around successfully inhibited me from speaking at all.

Eventually I began to feel cold. My head was still aching,

too—so I excused myself and walked quickly back to the house. "I still don't feel well: I'm going to try and get some sleep in the outhouse," I told my mother. "I shan't be disturbed so easily back there."

"It's all these welcoming functions: they've exhausted you," mother said severely. "They've really gone a bit too far! It would have given more than a headache to a man far fitter than you.... Do you think you have a fever coming on? You'd better let me get you some medicine and have a good long sleep...."

"No thank you, mother. I don't need any medicine, and there's no point in calling a doctor. When we were in the jungle we got to know a lot about our bodies and how to cure them, you know; we were on the watch for illness the whole time—we had to know how to look after ourselves."

"I dare say. But don't you think...?"

"Now, mother—please don't fuss! Believe me, I know what I'm talking about! I need neither medicine nor doctor. What I do need is a week's peace and quiet and I'll be back to normal. And the sooner you can send all these people away, the quicker I'll recover: all these questions are making my head worse and worse."

Mother looked tearful as she turned and went away. I was sorry to seem cruel, but I knew this was the only way: peace, quiet, rest, and dim lighting to soothe the nerves—that was what I needed!

I lost no time in slipping away to the outhouse. It felt fine to be on my own, away from all the bustle and all the questions. I didn't feel like eating, and I could tell that the fever was well on its way now.

I was feeling really cold and shivering quite violently. I took the bedding out of a cupboard and settled down. There was hardly any light in the room. The corridor that ran along the room faced the hills and I had only left one storm-shutter open; there was only the light from this one small space.

There were two rooms on the upstairs floor of the outhouse, each of them four yards square. I preferred the one nearest the steps.

I had two thick quilts over me now, but I was still shivering. I turned over on my back and looked up at the ceiling. I thought back twenty years—to the time when my father and I had put in the thick joists, plastered the walls, and fitted the tiles.

I remembered my father as tall for a Japanese. Just before I'd gone for my medical, ready for call-up, we'd measured each other's height and made marks on one of the pillars in the main house. Father turned out to be an inch shorter than I.

If only father had lived another three years.... It was quite unbearable, the thought of how happy he'd have been to see his son home alive.

I found myself talking to myself. "I don't believe in a spirit life, so, after he died, father's spirit couldn't come to visit me. Even so, by some sort of spiritual intuition, father might perhaps have comprehended that his son was still alive. He must have longed to find out the truth when the newspapers reported that I might still be alive after the seals signed Itō had been discovered by an aboriginal. And he'd gone to a village nearby, where there was somebody who'd been in Guam and had managed to get away alive, and had asked all about the course of the fighting there. Apparently his sciatica had brought him really low, but even so, he never gave up hope...."

There was a photograph of father in a frame hanging above the door to my left. In the photograph, he and mother were looking down on me as I slept; it was a photograph taken while I was still a baby. They were obviously very fond of each other.

"That noise," I told myself again; "it's the cows. I know very well that it's coming from the cowshed—but even so I can't help my nerves being all keyed-up." I don't suppose it should be imagined that our nervous system turned into a true *instinct* during our time in the jungle; but we got to

183

the point of reacting like any animal, all our senses alerted by the faintest noise. I suppose I shall get used to the old ways again, given time, but it would be something of a miracle if I found myself able to shake off sixteen years' experience and slip back into earlier habits after only a week or ten days! Are there any miracles in this world, though?

Those newspapermen—they were for ever using the word miracle; it was a miracle, they said, that Minakawa and I had got back to Japan alive. But man cannot live by miracles. No doubt if you asked Minakawa, he'd say there *is* such a thing as a miracle: but, as far as I'm concerned, whether there are miracles or not is a question of the same order as that evergreen about whether there's a God or not. I wonder how many hundreds of times Minakawa and I had it out in the jungle—with me arguing that there's no such thing as God. I used to go through the same old drill every time with him—"Japan's a poor country, and it has started a war relying on the support of a God who doesn't exist and a 'divine wind' that is a fiction. All these theories of Heaven-our-Helper and The-Spirit-Our-Support, and of the Descendant of the Deity being among us—they're all a lot of poppycock. It's theories like this that landed you and me in this fine corner of the world; yes, we've got Heaven-our-Helper and all that rubbish to thank for this desirable plot of Guam jungle!"

"It's all part of a grand design to make us believe in God, to fortify our hearts and help us stand out against these hardships," Minakawa would reply. Once a man gets bitten by the bug, you can't win!

The noise started up again: it was the cows rubbing their heads against the manger.

I turned over in bed. I could feel that my whole nervous system was taut and strained. I'd got to get myself relaxed and back to normal as quickly as I could.

It was about three o'clock in the afternoon. Suddenly I was startled out of my half-waking reveries by the sound of the door opening downstairs. I jerked myself up, ready to move for cover.

"How do you feel now? Did you manage to sleep a little?" It was mother's voice; she was climbing the stairs as she spoke.

She was carrying a bowl, and she put it down gently by the edge of my pillow. There was a milk gruel in it. "You've not eaten a thing, you know, and that's not the way to treat your body. You're not going to get any better till you start eating."

"I just don't feel like eating anything, I'm afraid."

I lay down again, and mother smoothed and tidied the quilts and pulled them round my shoulders. Then she felt my forehead. I closed my eyes. "I think it would be better to have the doctor come and . . ."

"I'm all *right*. Please try not to fuss quite so much. When we got this sort of thing in the jungle, we managed to cure ourselves just by sleeping it off—and on the bare ground."

I turned my face so that I could see her. She was staring straight through me, almost as if her eyes were fixed on some distant point far beyond me. I suddenly realised that she couldn't take much more of this talk of the jungle. I told myself I must stop talking, for a while at least, about the jungle and all the hardships there'd been.

"I doubt if we'll get any of those newsmen today. I got well and truly angry with the whole lot of them last night."

I learned later that she had really gone for one of them the previous evening. He was a broadcaster and he'd even pushed his way into the outhouse and got right to my bedside, microphone and all!

Mother took the bowl and went off down the steps. I closed my eyes again, and at once my thoughts went to Minakawa. He'd have arrived at his home today. At this very moment, he was probably being fêted and welcomed just as I had been; there'd be the same speeches, the same banners, the same bouquets, the same crowds, the same jostling. Like me, even in his wildest dreams, Minakawa would never have imagined himself being given such a welcome.

I was dreaming. I was back on Guam. Sirens were wailing all over the island. Then the crump of the heavy guns.

I'm pretty sure of the date—it was in January, 1953.

Minakawa and I, startled by all the noise and clatter, crept out of our shelters to try and see what it was all about. It was night-time; there was no moon, but the sky was clear and full of stars. I remember that, to get a better view, Minakawa made his way to the rocky part of the hill which was free from scrub, and spent the whole night there trying to make sense of what was happening.

"It's an air-raid warning, surely?" said Minakawa. But all we heard was six or seven explosions from the big guns, then everything went still and quiet.

"This is the counter-attack by a fresh Japanese army, at last," I said.

"This is it at last. It's been a long wait. But it proves what we've always believed—the war is still going on," said Minakawa.

I was too hepped up to keep control of myself. We'd neither of us noticed in our excitement that we were raising our voices. And there we were, too overjoyed to conceal ourselves, sitting out in the open on the rocks, our arms round each other's shoulders. It had been a long time since we'd been so buoyed up, since we'd cared so little about concealing ourselves.

"When our planes and naval guns start a bombardment, do you think we'll be all right here? Might we not be in the range of the bombs and shells?"

"No. We'll be safe enough—there's no fear that we shall end up killed by our own bombs or guns. They'll be after the American batteries and troop concentrations; we're far enough from them to be out of harm's way." Minakawa seemed to have considerable confidence in the accuracy of our barrage. Still, he'd been trained on trench mortars, and I expect he knew what he was talking about.

186

"I suppose you're right. Still, even so, we'd be in a mess if something started while we were fast asleep."

"All right, then. When our task force comes into the attack, and the barrage starts up and gets really hot, let's take turns to keep watch shall we? Can you remember the old regulations for the night watch?"

"Yes ... I can—quite clearly."

It was war that had thrust us into these warped and distorted circumstances: and we no doubt considered that it was only by war that we would or could be rescued from them. This was the way we thought about it—the way we'd been taught to think about it. Once we'd been sucked into the world of the soldier, there was no way of getting out of it by our own efforts of mind.

We continued to hold out this hope of a Japanese landing for a full two years—even though all the hullabaloo turned out to be only an American exercise. When there were no more sirens to be heard, when there was no more firing, the flame of hope at length began to flicker and die.

When you've been robbed of a hope that you've clung to for two long years, you're dealt a mental blow that it takes a lot to live through. We both noticed that, soon after the final disabusing of our fond hopes, we started thinking more and more about our age: in fact, I'm sure you can put the two things together—it was because we'd been robbed of all hope that we began to think how old we were getting.

"God! I'm thirty-five now..." I'd say to myself, looking back across the empty years of youth.

And now, as I write, I keep on realising that the figure has grown to thirty nine.

6

Epitaph

These reminiscences have been written in the dimly-lit upper story of the outhouse my father and I built together twenty years ago. Somehow, it seems the only place where I can feel really at ease—perhaps because it's a world apart from everything, and the years I spent away from home were also spent in a world divorced from ordinary, everyday society—a world that used up and wasted my youth.

In the jungles of Guam, I had been forced to adopt the ways of an animal, beyond the limits within which—one would have thought—a man could have stayed alive at all. There were many who had lost all balance, who had failed to come to terms with the jungle: one after another, the jungle claimed their lives. As we watched, we realised that we must learn a whole new set of values, adopt a whole new range of techniques for keeping alive and keeping sane.

One by one, Minakawa and I acquired these new arts— by perseverence, by patience, and especially through the help of the understanding and tolerance that grew from our deepening friendship. I suppose nobody would describe the way of life we eventually evolved as in any way *human*; but for us, at least, it was a form of living. It at least gave us survival—and for me this meant survival to pick up the threads of country life surrounded once again by the hills and rivers of the valley where I was born.

But once it has taken hold, the jungle will not so easily let go. . . .

At night-time, I'm instantly wide-awake with the slightest noise or movement, ears and eyes on the alert, straining and searching to identify the sound and then locate it. A second or two afterwards, of course, the panic subsides; all this tension relaxes as soon as I discover what caused the sound—a calf moving or something of the sort. But before I've made the discovery, during that split second of tension and strain, all my senses are trying to stimulate and arouse me by telling me that there is danger on the way: then, once this short period is passed, I understand well enough that there's not the slightest element of danger in the situation; *but my senses won't acknowledge this conclusion.*

So my problem is this discrepancy between what my senses tell me and what I know to be the case. I realise that my first task in life from now on is to re-train my senses, and take them back to pre-jungle circumstances and reactions. I have to start learning to live all over again. God knows how long this rehabilitation will take: but it has got to be achieved successfully....

Yesterday, I had a female visitor. She said she'd come to renew acquaintance with me—she'd read all about our discovery and our safe return in the newspaper.

"But I just can't remember where we met, or how..." I said, in all honesty.

"There's something that makes it certain I shan't ever forget you."

I was getting more and more bewildered and flustered by all these hints.

"It was when you were posted from the unit at Kōfu to the Amur River in Manchuria."

I thought back to the Amur River and our positions on the border with Russia; but there wasn't a single woman involved in any of my memories of the place. "Yes, I was with a unit on the Amur. It was in about 1942, I'd say." I was thinking furiously as I spoke.

"There was a period then, was there, when you were on guard duty at a clothing depôt?"

"M'm. Maybe there was."

"I wonder if you remember that you once struck one of

the civilian women attached to the depôt?" As she spoke, she looked me straight in the face; her eyes were absolutely brimming over with fun.

"I was slapped twice—once on each cheek; you said I'd not bowed to you." She laughed as she said this, and put her hands up to her cheeks, the tips of her fingers resting lightly on the bones.

"Oh! *I* remember! Yes; I've got it now! I remember, now, thinking how tiny you were after I'd slapped you."

"I'm still tiny today, don't you think?" There wasn't the slightest trace of anger in her voice.

"I'm sorry. It was very wrong of me."

"I got married very soon after that. Your unit had been moved to Peian by then."

"You stayed in Manchuria, then?"

She nodded.

"What happened to you when the war ended?"

"I was repatriated fairly quickly. But my husband is dead...."

My head was hurting now. There really wasn't anything more to talk about.

But her questions went on and on; and we talked about the jungle, because this is all I can talk about nowadays.

Last night she slept in the outhouse; this is where I always sleep now, and we each had one of the upstairs rooms. I got myself tucked in and all ready to try to get some sleep, but she still jabbered on through the partition.

She was talking not about Manchuria, or about the war— but woman's talk. This was the very first time I'd heard a woman talking woman's talk. I was terrified: any minute she'd be working the conversation round so that she could start putting out feelers about marriage! I found I didn't want anything from her; she had nothing to offer me, mentally or physically.

My head was aching again. I fled to the main house and spent the rest of the night there. I hardly slept. I kept tossing and turning and couldn't get my thoughts away from my wasted youth. That night, with the woman in bed over in my outhouse, and me not wanting anything from her, I felt all the more strongly that my youth had been dashed from my hands and was rotting away in the earth of Guam....

This morning, at dawn, I was back at the shrine, standing in front of my own grave and reading again the inscription on the tombstone:

> *Itō Masashi, born 1st March, 1921, the*
> *eldest son of Itō Tanuki (deceased).*
> *Entered Primary Department of Furuseki*
> *Higher Normal School, April, 1927; graduated*
> *March, 1935.*
> *Entered Kōfu Middle School, April 1935;*
> *completed the course, March, 1936.*
> *Awarded Fourth Dan Belt by the President*
> *of the Yamanashi Judo Society, 1935.*
> *Passed conscription tests with merit, 1941.*
> *Joined the Colours with the 63rd Regiment*
> *at Kōfu, January, 1942.*
> *Posted to the Amur River Zone in Manchuria,*
> *April, 1942.*
> *Moved to Peian Province, Manchuria, April, 1943.*
> *Killed in action on Guam Island, at the age of*
> *twenty-three, September 30th, 1944.*
>
> *Erected in his memory by his Father, at the*
> *Autumn Equinox, 1953.*

But which of us is telling the truth: the returned soldier claiming so desperately to be alive; or the tombstone asserting his death in the jungles of Guam?

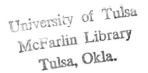